THE SHAPING OF THE ISLE OF WIGHT

Cover: Whale Chine;
Overleaf: Fig.1: Geological sketch-map (based on information from the
British Geological Survey Isle of Wight Special Sheet).

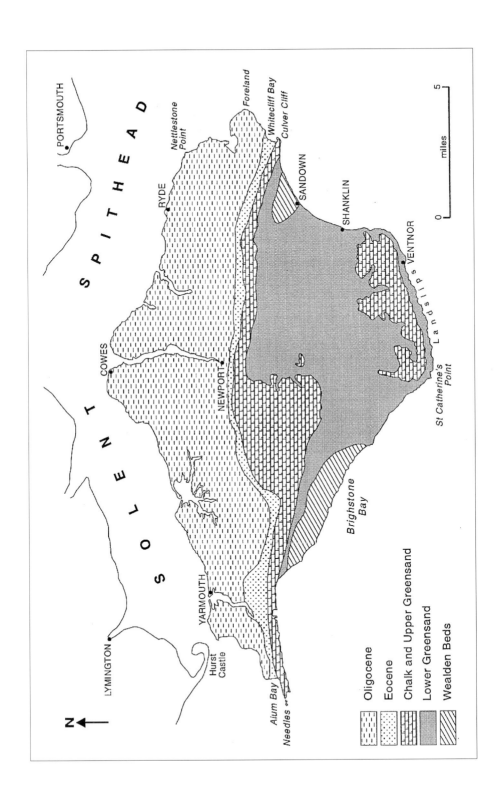

The SHAPING
of the
ISLE OF WIGHT

with an Excursion Guide

Eric Bird

EX LIBRIS PRESS

Published in 1997 by
EX LIBRIS PRESS
1 The Shambles
Bradford on Avon
Wiltshire

Design and typesetting by Ex Libris Press

Cover printed by
Shires Press, Trowbridge

Printed and bound in Britain by
Cromwell Press, Broughton Gifford, Wiltshire

ISBN 0 948578 83 1

Contents

LANDFORM EVOLUTION

THE EXCURSIONS

AROUND THE COAST

INLAND EXCURSIONS

Preface

This book is the outcome of my interest in the geology and scenery of the Isle of Wight, sustained over many years by numerous visits to the island. It was here that I was introduced to Geology, on a weekend field excursion conducted by the Lyell Club of King's College London, in October 1950, based at Sandown Youth Hostel. My recollection is that on the Saturday we were led along the shore eastward to look at the rock succession from the Wealden up to the Chalk under Culver Cliff, then over Bembridge Down to Whitecliff Bay and northward to see the Oligocene beds. On Sunday we were taken by coach across to Whale Chine, where we walked along the shore to Atherfield Point to see the Lower Greensand and overlying Wealden formations, then to Alum Bay to see the Lower Tertiary formations.

I recall being fascinated by the variations in colour and texture of the various rock formations, and the drama of the strong folding that had left some of them standing vertically, but I could find little enthusiasm for fossil and mineral hunting. It was on a later excursion, to the Isle of Purbeck in Dorset, that I began to understand the relationships between rock formations and the land surface features that are the concern of geomorphologists, and since then my interest in geology has been as a background to geomorphology, the study of landforms. That interest led, many years later, to my book on the *Geology and Scenery of Dorset*, also published by Ex Libris Press in 1995, and now to this guide to the shaping of the Isle of Wight.

Geologists often advocate fossil hunting or searching for minerals as a way of stimulating interest in their subject, but these can be damaging and dangerous activities. In my view a geological map is intrinsically interesting, not least because of its challenge to visualise formations and structures in three dimensions. Once the relationships between geological outcrops and land surface features are appreciated they add to the enjoyment of a walk or drive through the countryside, or of looking at a landscape from a viewpoint.

The Isle of Wight is particularly interesting from this point of view because of the intricacy of its geology and the variety of its landforms.

It has long been a Mecca for geologists, and among those who have worked on the island are H.H. Bristow, Clement Reid, A. Strahan and H.J. Osborne White, all of whom produced Geological Memoirs. More recently Brian Daley, Allan Insole, D.J. Stewart and N. Edwards have published important research, and there have been several expeditions by the Geologists' Association. Curiously, the island has received only incidental attention from geomorphologists, a deficiency that this book would like to remedy by promoting further research.

The Isle of Wight also presents landscapes that have stimulated artists and writers*. J.M.W. Turner made the first of his many landscape paintings here, a view of the Needles in 1793, and Myles Birket Foster, Edward William Cooke, William Gray and Helen Allingham are among the many other artists who have painted island landscapes. Writers include Henry James, Francis Kilvert, C.J. Cornish and Charles Dickens. The poet Algernon Charles Swinburne lived and wrote here, and had a famous adventure climbing Culver Cliff, while Alfred Lord Tennyson made Farringford House, near Freshwater Bay, his home and wrote many poems on the island. Others with local associations are Keats, Longfellow, Wordsworth and W.H. Auden, whose poem beginning 'Look Stranger, on this island now', written as a commentary for a film about the Isle of Wight, told of where 'the chalk wall falls to the foam, and its tall ledges oppose the pluck and knock of the tide'.

There are many visitors to the Isle of Wight each year. Some relish the commercial attractions of Blackgang and Alum Bay, but many come to enjoy the ambience of an island that is generally quieter and less crowded than the rest of Southern England. There are good bus and train services, particularly in summer, and fine opportunities for cycling, or walking the impressive network of public footpaths. A journey through the island's landscapes or around its coastline is a good way of appreciating the links between geology and scenery.

This book follows a similar pattern to my *Geology and Scenery of Dorset*, with introductory chapters explaining the geology and evolution of landforms, followed by guides to a coastal excursion and twelve inland excursions. I hope it will lead people to explore the island, and enjoy it as much as I have done.

See Eric Bird and Lilian James (1993) Writers on the Coast. *Windrush Press, Gloucestershire:* 144-173.

Acknowledgements

I am grateful to Lilian Modlock for helping me gather information on the Isle of Wight, and Steve Hutt of the Geological Museum, Sandown, for discussing geological problems. Chandra Jayasuriya and Catherine Vinot drew the diagrams. Figures 1, 2, 3, 4 and 5 contain information reproduced by permission of the Director, British Geological Survey: NERC copyright reserved.

Eric Bird
Mottistone, I.O.W.
September 1996

Legal Notice

Reference is made on pages 71-2 and 142 to various hazards to be recognised when carrying out field work in the Isle of Wight. The publisher and author accept no responsibility for any personal injury or fatality or damage of any kind suffered by a person as a direct or indirect result of anyone following a route or path suggested or referred to herein.

ERA	PERIOD		AGE	EPOCH
CAINOZOIC	Quaternary		10,000 y	Holocene (Recent)
			2 my	Pleistocene
	Tertiary	Eogene	5 my	Pliocene
			23 my	Miocene
		Palaeo-gene	36 my	Oligocene
			53 my	Eocene
				Palaeocene
			65 my	
MESOZOIC	Cretaceous		144 my	
	Jurassic		213 my	
	Triassic		248 my	
PALAEOZOIC	Permian		290 my	
	Carboniferous		360 my	
	Devonian		405 my	
	Silurian		436 my	
	Ordivician		510 my	
	Cambrian		560 my	
PRE-CAMBRIAN				

Table 1: The Geological Column
my = million years

INTRODUCTION

The Isle of Wight is often described as having the shape of a diamond, a lozenge, or a parallelogram with slightly concave margins. It extends about 23.5 miles (37.8 km) from the Needles in the west to the Foreland in the east and 13.3 miles (21.4 km) from Egypt Point at Cowes in the north to St. Catherine's Point in the south, and has an area of about 150 square miles (388 sq. km). It is separated from the mainland (Hampshire) by a marine strait known as The Solent to the north-west and Spithead to the north-east. The coastline (excluding estuaries) is about 56 miles (90 km) long.

The traveller or holidaymaker who wants to study the scenery of the Isle of Wight should first look at the Ordnance Survey Outdoor Leisure sheet 29 on a scale of 1 : 25,000, and the British Geological Survey Special Sheet, which shows the outcrops of rock formations on a scale of 1: 50,000. The British Geological Survey has also produced a simplified Holiday Geology Map of the Isle of Wight at a scale of about 1: 90,000, superimposed on a satellite view, with a brief key to the main formations. This gives a good general picture of the island geology, but it lacks the local detail necessary for the interpretation of some of the smaller landforms.

This book explores the scenery of the Isle of Wight in relation to the underlying geological formations (Fig. 1). It is an account of the geomorphology of the island: the evolution of its landforms – the hills and valleys, escarpments and plateaux of the existing landscape, together with the bordering coastline. These have been shaped by erosion and deposition, resulting from rainfall and runoff into rivers, the effects of frost and snow, wind action, and waves and currents in the sea. Landform evolution has been guided by geological factors, such as lithology (the type of rock) and structure (the arrangement of rock formations). Geologists are also interested in the mineral content of rocks (mineralogy) and the fossil forms they contain (palaeontology), but for geomorphologists the lithology and structure are more relevant.

Geology

Geological time is divided into four eras, each comprising periods and epochs, as shown in Table 1. On the Isle of Wight the formations are of Mesozoic and Cainozoic age, spanning the Cretaceous, Tertiary and Quaternary periods (Table 2). Details of the various subdivisions on the Isle of Wight shown on the 1: 50,000 British Geological Survey map are described in the British Geological

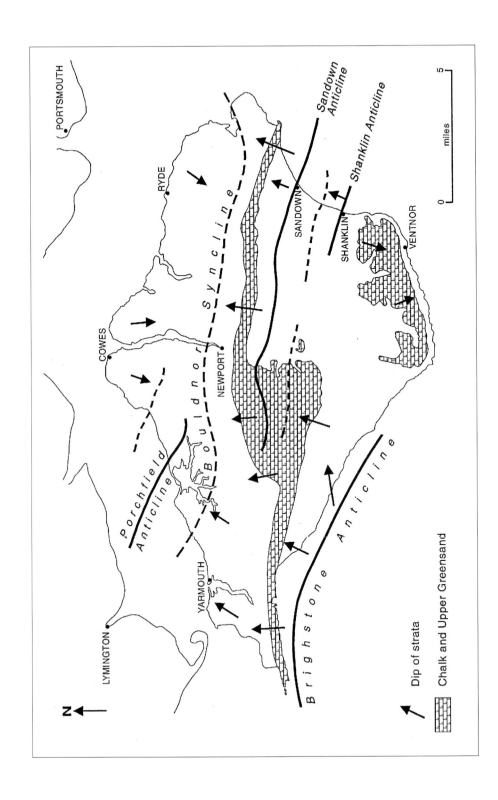

N

LYMINGTON

PORTSMOUTH

RYDE

COWES

NEWPORT

YARMOUTH

SANDOWN

SHANKLIN

VENTNOR

Porchfield Anticline

Brighstone Anticline

B o u l d n o r   S y n c l i n e

Sandown Anticline

Shanklin Anticline

Dip of strata

Chalk and Upper Greensand

0   miles   5

Survey Memoir, *A Short Account of the Geology of the Isle of Wight*[1]. At the edge of the geological map is a column showing the names, the sequence and the thicknesses of the rock formations found on the island. Subsequently, in order to conform with international rules, some of the names of geological formations have been changed: the new names are used in the Geologists' Association Guide to the Isle of Wight[2]. As far as possible these will be used in this book, but there is the difficulty that the British Geological Survey map uses the earlier scheme, and it has been necessary to retain some of the previous names (Table 2).

The geological map also shows the angle at which the rock formations are tilted (the dip), indicated by arrows, often with the gradient in degrees. From this it is possible to deduce the pattern of folding, with up-arched anticlines and down-warped synclines running roughly west to east through the island (Fig. 2). A distinction is made between solid formations, up to and including those that formed in the Tertiary period, and superficial (drift) formations, which are mainly of Quaternary (i.e. Pleistocene and Holocene) age. The outcrops of solid formations are partly obscured by various kinds of superficial deposits.

Physical Features

The main topographic feature of the Isle of Wight is a Chalk ridge, known as the Central Downs, running from The Needles eastward to Culver Cliff. As the 1: 25,000 topographic map shows, the crest of the ridge rises to between 100 and just over 200 metres above mean sea level[3], the highest point being 214 metres on Brighstone Down (433847)*. For much of its length this is a steep-sided 'hogsback' ridge, less than half a mile wide, because the Chalk (about 500 metres thick) dips steeply (up to 85°) northward, so that its outcrop is not much wider than its total thickness. There is a south-facing escarpment cut across the edges of the steeply-dipping Chalk, and a similar north-facing back-slope[4], declining in the general direction of the dip. However, there is an area

---

*Six-figure Grid Reference numbers can be used to locate places on the Ordnance Survey 1 : 25,000 map of the Isle of Wight. They are obtained by taking the number of the western boundary of the grid square and estimating tenths eastward, then taking the number of the southern boundary of the grid square and estimating tenths northward. Thus Godshill church is in the grid square with 52 as its western boundary and 81 as its southern boundary. It lies 7 tenths eastward from 52 and 8 tenths northward from 81. Its grid reference is therefore 527818.

Opposite: Fig. 2: Geological structures (based on information from the British Geological Survey Isle of Wight Special Sheet).

south-west of Newport where the dip declines to less than 10°, and as the sketch-map (Fig. 1) shows, the Chalk outcrop widens to about four miles, the escarpment continuing along its southern margin.

North of the Chalk ridge is a gently undulating lowland on Lower Tertiary formations (Palaeocene and Eocene), with a very steep (70°-90°) northward dip close to the Downs, declining to almost horizontal in the overlying Oligocene beds, as shown in Fig. 3. There are minor ridges, spurs and plateaux, some with a capping of superficial gravel deposits.

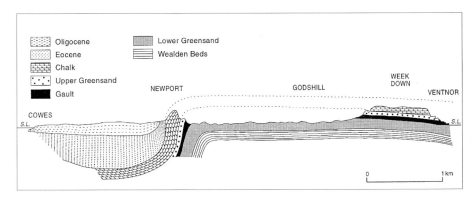

Fig. 3: Cross-section of the central part of the Isle of Wight showing the relationship between surface features and geological formations.

South of the Chalk ridge is a more irregular lowland, bordered by often steep slopes of Upper Greensand, overlooking wide undulating country on the Gault clay and Lower Greensand, within which there are minor ridges on harder sandstones. In the south-west, behind Brighstone Bay, and in the east, north of Sandown, are lowlands on the underlying Wealden Beds, brought up in the crests of the Brighstone and Sandown Anticlines (Figs. 4 and 5).

In the southern part of the island the Chalk returns, dipping gently southward, and forming an escarpment backed by the Southern Plateau, which rises more than 200 metres above sea level, the highest point being 240 metres on St. Boniface Down (568785). This plateau has been dissected by headwaters of the Medina and Eastern Yar rivers to form deeply incised valleys, bordered by steep slopes in the Chalk and Upper Greensand, the gradient diminishing on the Gault clay and the Lower Greensand below. There have been landslides (known locally as landslips) of Chalk and Upper Greensand over the Gault clay along the escarpment, and also along the southern flank, where there has been massive slumping, with tumbled rock masses extending down to the shore between St. Catherine's Point and Luccombe Bay. An upper cliff of Chalk and

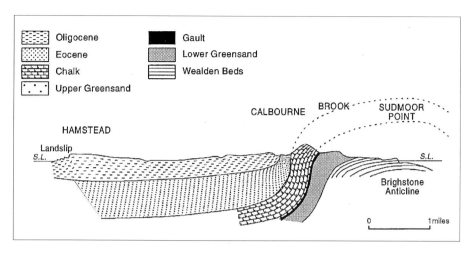

Above, Fig 4: Cross-section of the eastern part of the Isle of Wight showing the relationship between surface features and geological formations.

Below, Fig. 5: Cross-section of the western part of the Isle of Wight showing the relationship between surface features and geological formations.

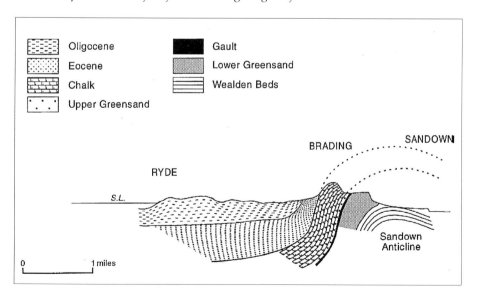

Upper Greensand overlooks a subsided fringe or Undercliff, where from time to time continuing instability is marked by active landslides.

The river systems of the Isle of Wight are dominated by parallel northward-flowing streams, notably the Medina and the Eastern and Western Yar, each of which has cut gaps through the Central Downs. Several smaller streams also run northward from the Central Downs, and all of them flow into estuaries that open to the Solent and Spithead.

The coastline of the Isle of Wight has features related to outcrops of the geological formations listed in Table 2. The Central Downs terminate in promontories of Chalk extending out to the stacks known as The Needles in the west, and bold Culver Cliff in the east. To the north are bays excavated into the narrow outcrop of the soft, steeply-dipping Palaeocene and Eocene sands and clays; Alum Bay in the west and Whitecliff Bay in the east. Beyond these the coastline is cut into the generally soft Oligocene formations, which form slumping bluffs and eroding cliffs on the clays and marls, with some bolder cliffs and shore platforms on the limestones, particularly the Bembridge Limestone, which outcrops as ledges off the Foreland on the eastern coast. The cliffs and bluffs are interrupted by valley-mouth inlets, as at Yarmouth, Newtown, Cowes, Wootton and Bembridge Harbour, which are typically estuaries with bordering tidal marshlands, and there are smaller alluvial plains at Thorness, Gurnard, King's Quay, Ryde and Seaview.

On the south-west coast there are high cliffs where the Chalk and Upper Greensand escarpment has been undercut by marine erosion between Scratchell's Bay and Compton Bay, and also on the Lower Greensand. Cliffs have also been cut into the soft Wealden clays and marls along the shore of Brighstone Bay, across the Atherfield Clay at Atherfield Point, and in the sands and sandstones of the Lower Greensand, the rapid cliff recession at Blackgang being accompanied by major landslides.

A similar sequence is seen on the south-east coast, west from the Chalk at Culver Cliff and the Lower Greensand at Red Cliff. The coast declines along the lowland on the soft Wealden clays and marls at Sandown, then rises again to cliffs in Lower Greensand southward to Shanklin and Luccombe Bay. As already noted, the southern coast between Luccombe Bay and St. Catherine's Point is dominated by an upper cliff in Chalk and Upper Greensand overlooking irregular landslide topography which descends to a bouldery cliffed coastline, parts of which have been stabilised by sea walls.

Nautical charts show that the sea floor around the Isle of Wight generally slopes gently away from the coast. To the north, the Solent and Spithead contain a series of narrow troughs with depths of 20 to 30 metres, and there is a deep scour hole in the north-west, between Cliff End and Hurst Castle spit, attaining a depth of 56 metres. The Shingles are a large triangular bank of gravel in shallow water south-west of Hurst Castle, patches of which emerge as the tide falls. Off The Needles, and round the south coast to Culver Cliff the sea floor declines to a depth of 10 metres just under a mile (1.5 km) offshore, the slope steepening off the high coast between St. Catherine's Point and Dunnose. The sea floor profile is generally concave, the gradient diminishing to depths of 30 to 40 metres 10 kilometres offshore.

Mean spring tide range on the north coast increases from 2.6 metres at Yarmouth to 3.6 metres at Cowes and 3.8 metres at Ryde, but declines in the estuaries: 2.5 metres at Newport. On the east and south-east coasts it is just over 3 metres at Ventnor and 3.5 metres at Sandown . On the south-west coast spring tide range diminishes to 2.1 metres in Freshwater Bay, and on the west coast it is 2.2 metres in Totland Bay. The intertidal zone around the island is generally sandy or rocky and 50 to 100 metres wide, but along the north coast it becomes wider with mud as well as sand, and only a few rocky sectors. Off Ryde the sandy intertidal zone widens to more than a kilometre at the lowest tides. Tidal currents around the island are generally weak, rarely more than 3 knots (5.6 km/hr), occasionally intensified by strong wind and wave action.

Wave action is strong on the west and south-west coasts, which are exposed to the prevailing south-westerly waves in the English Channel, and on the south coast between St. Catherine's Point and Dunnose, where there is relatively deep water close inshore. The south-east coast, between Dunnose and Sandown, is less open to south-westerly waves, but receives occasional strong waves from the south and south-east. As the coast curves eastward under Culver Cliff, exposure to south-westerly waves again increases. On the north-east and north coasts wave action is much weaker because of the short fetch (extent of water across which waves can be generated) across Spithead and the Solent, and because northerly winds are less frequent and rarely strong. Waves are also less effective on the north and north-east coasts because the intertidal zone (i.e. between high and low tide lines) is relatively wide and the nearshore waters shallow, so that wave energy is dissipated and waves reach the back of the shore only at high tide.

Geomorphology

An understanding of the relationships between landforms and geological formations adds to the interest and enjoyment of landscapes, especially when they are as varied and intricate as those of the Isle of Wight. Events millions of years ago produced the geological formations that now influence the 'lie of the land', so that in order to understand the present landscape it is necessary to make a journey into the geological past[5]. Some landforms have been shaped gradually by weathering[6] and erosion over many thousands of years. Others have developed rapidly: sudden landslides after very wet weather, or a cliff cut back rapidly during a storm.

There is often a simple correlation between landscape features and the outcrops of rock formations shown on the geological map. Boundaries between geological formations are sometimes marked by changes of slope, particularly where there are sharp contrasts, as between hard sandstone or limestone and soft clay. On the northern side of the Central Downs, for example, the Upper Chalk forms a steep slope descending to pass beneath the clays of the Reading Beds, the gradient diminishing abruptly: the contrast is accentuated by the fact that these formations also dip very steeply. The Upper Greensand escarpment declines to low-lying, often wet terrain on the Gault clay, but there is a steep, often cliffy, slope on the outcrop of the chert beds high in the Upper Greensand. There are ridges and scarps on minor formations within the Ferruginous Sands of the Lower Greensand, and within the Wealden Beds, some corresponding with outcrops not shown on the geological map.

The topographic expression of geological formations also depends on the texture of dissection of the landscape by river valleys. Geological contrasts produce well-defined landforms in dissected areas, but are suppressed on interfluvial plateaux or planed-down lowlands.

Geomorphology provides a background for the study of soils and vegetation, and the landscape patterns resulting from past and present human activities – how the land is used, the effects of quarrying, and the impacts of man-made structures and communications. The influence of geology on the landscape has been emphasised where local rocks have been used as building materials, some of the villages and farmhouses on the Isle of Wight strongly reflecting their local geological heritage[7].

Exploring the Isle of Wight

The varied and intricate geology and scenery of the Isle of Wight can be explored by car or on a bicycle, following roads shown on the Ordnance Survey Outdoor Leisure Map, or by walking the lanes and footpaths shown on this map[8]. Outcrops shown on geological maps can be traced in the field, and formations exposed in coastal cliffs can be seen by walking along the shore at low tide, or from viewpoints along the coastline. Inland, many features are best seen on clear days in winter, when views are less obstructed by foliage on trees and hedgerows.

Plan of the book

This book seeks to provide people who come to enjoy the scenery of the Isle of Wight with information on the geology and geomorphology. Chapter 2 describes the geological formations present, and explains how they originated. The outcrops of solid formations are progressively older in sequence when traced from north to south, the youngest (the Cranmore Beds of the Upper Oligocene) being in the north-west, between Yarmouth and Newtown Harbour, and the oldest (the Wessex Shales of the Lower Cretaceous) in Brighstone Bay, and to a lesser extent near Sandown.

Chapter 3 examines how the landforms of the Isle of Wight have developed, identifying stages in their evolution and describing the processes that have shaped the present scenery.

Chapter 4 describes the geomorphological and related geological features encountered in a journey around the coastline, and Chapter 5 gives details of a dozen inland excursions, some by car, others on foot. Footpaths are numbered in the Isle of Wight, with key letters referring to local regions, but the system is complicated because the numbers change frequently, especially at regional boundaries. Unfortunately, the footpath numbers are not shown on the 1:25,000 map, and they are not always included on signposts in the landscape, so the walking itineraries use six-figure grid references (p. 15) to locate key points.

Places mentioned in other chapters are either located by grid references in the text, or can be found by obtaining grid references from the Index. Superscript numbers in the text indicate items in the Notes (pages 168-170) which give details of relevant publications and additional comments for more specialised readers. Technical terms are defined on first use (see Index for first page references).

ERA	FORMATION		THICKNESS
QUATERNARY & PLIOCENE	Superficial Deposits		various
OLIGOCENE	Hamstead Beds		80 m
	Bembridge Marls		20-37 m
	Bembridge Limestone		0.5-8 m
	Osborne Beds		22-33 m
	Headon Beds		45-65 m
EOCENE	Barton Sand		27-63 m
	Barton Clay		48-76 m
	Bracklesham Beds		174-178 m
	Bagshot Beds		23-42 m
	London Clay		94-119 m
	Oldhaven Beds		2.8-4.3 m
PALAEOCENE	Reading Beds		27-49 m
CRETACEOUS	Upper Chalk		311-404 m
	Middle Chalk		45-59 m
	Lower Chalk		49-64 m
	Upper Greensand		30-40 m
	Gault		29-31 m
	Lower Greensand	Carstone	2.22 m
		Sandrock Beds	27-56 m
		Ferruginous Sands	152-155 m
		Atherfield Clay	18-33 m
	Wealden Beds	Vectis Shales	about 59 m
		Wessex Marls	about 168 m

Table 2: Geological Formations
Typical range of thicknesses in the Isle of Wight in metres (from various sources).

ISLE OF WIGHT GEOLOGY

Introduction

The geological formations found in the Isle of Wight (Table 2) are all sedimentary rocks. They consist of deposits that were laid down on the floor of the sea, in estuaries and on deltas, or in lakes and lagoons in Cretaceous and early Tertiary times. They include clays, silts, sands and sandstones, limestones, and some gravels. The various formations were originally deposited in more or less horizontal strata, but have since been tilted, folded and in places faulted by earth (tectonic) movements, forming structures that were then dissected by erosion to produce the present landscape. Deep borings have encountered the older (Jurassic) rocks, which are doubtless underlain by Triassic and Palaeozoic formations equivalent to those that emerge westward in Dorset, Devon and Cornwall, but the land surface of the Isle of Wight comprises outcrops of formations deposited during the Cretaceous and early Tertiary periods.

The characteristics of each rock formation indicate the kind of environment in which it was deposited. Some rocks are of marine origin (i.e. laid down in the sea), indicated by minerals that form in sea water and fossil remains of organisms that lived in the sea, such as marine species of fish and shells. Others were deposited in estuaries and lagoons, and others in fresh water, as shown by the presence of fossils of species that inhabited such environments. Superficial deposits were strewn across the land surface in late Tertiary and Quaternary times.

Coarse sediments (sand and gravel) have usually been derived from a steep, uplifted hinterland, while fine sediments (silt and clay) imply that the adjacent land was low lying, drained by gentler rivers. Limestones were formed in clear seas during episodes of warm and dry climate, whereas thick clays were often the product of muddy rivers draining from warm and wet catchments. A transition or sudden contrast in sediment type in a succession of rocks indicates an environmental change, such as the deepening or shallowing of the receiving sea, uplift or subsidence of the adjacent land, the arrival of a warmer, cooler, wetter or drier climate, or changes in the vegetation cover.

Cretaceous

The Cretaceous formations seen on the Isle of Wight begin with the Wealden Beds, sands and clays seen in the cliffs of Brighstone Bay and Compton Bay in the south-west of the island, and behind Sandown Bay in the south-east. They form lowlands. The Wealden Beds are overlain by the Lower and Upper Greensand, both of which form bordering ridges and escarpments, and the intervening Gault clay, usually excavated as a valley. The Upper Greensand is overlain in turn by the thick white limestone known as Chalk, which has a narrow, steeply-dipping outcrop in the Central Downs, and a wider outcrop in the Southern Plateau, an upland with a north-facing escarpment and a gentler southward slope that declines in the direction of the dip.

The Cretaceous outcrops match those of southern Dorset, especially in the so-called Isle of Purbeck, where underlying Jurassic formations are also seen[9]. They also occur in and around the Weald, in south-east England, exposed by the unroofing and denudation of geological formations in a broad anticline which repeats on a larger scale the features seen on and south of the Central Downs of the Isle of Wight. Cretaceous outcrops can also be traced through the Weymouth Lowland in Dorset, and from there northward, with bold Chalk and Upper Greensand escarpments overlooking the Jurassic country of West Dorset, and on through Wessex to the Chilterns and East Anglia; then north of The Wash through Lincolnshire to the Yorkshire Wolds, where the Chalk escarpment ends in the cliffs of Flamborough Head.

Tertiary

Lower Tertiary rocks, mainly sandstones and clays, with some limestones, dip steeply off the Central Downs Chalk, and occupy the broad lowland in the northern half of the Isle of Wight. The dip diminishes rapidly northwards, but is complicated by minor anticlines and synclines. The deposits represent phases of deltaic and estuarine accretion, interrupted when marine clays were deposited in briefly transgressing seas. The sequence of solid formations ends abruptly in the Oligocene, when a prolonged phase of denudation of rocks and structures began, leading to the shaping of the present topography. There are various superficial deposits, some of which formed (or began to form) in Upper Tertiary times, while others are of Quaternary age.

The Tertiary deposits of the Isle of Wight are similar to those in Hampshire and Dorset, and also in the London Basin, along the valley of the Thames.

Quaternary

The Quaternary spans the last two million years of geological time, and comprises the Pleistocene and the Holocene (the past 10,000 years). The Pleistocene had periods of much colder climate, when glaciers expanded into Britain, and the Isle of Wight had a periglacial environment, with frequent and prolonged frosts and extensive snowfalls alternating with brief summer thaws, much like the conditions now found in northernmost Norway or Baffin Island in Canada. Vegetation was sparse, and of tundra type. Rock outcrops were exposed and shattered by repeated freezing and thawing, and the disintegrated material (mainly gravel and sand) was sludged down slopes by repeated freezing and thawing and the recurrent melting of a snow cover. The outcome was the formation and deposition of angular gravels, mainly of flint and chert, some of which persist in upland areas and on the crests of lowland hills. At the same time, silt and clay were mobilised by winds blowing across dry unvegetated land areas, and deposited as sheets of loamy brickearth, patches of which can be found as superficial drift deposits.

There were intervening milder (interglacial, or interperiglacial) periods, when the Isle of Wight became vegetated, and its surface was shaped by runoff from rainfall and occasional snow, producing rivers which carved out valleys and deposited some of the derived sediment, including gravel, sand, silt and clay, downstream on valley floors, some of which were later dissected into river terraces with cappings of the older associated river sediments (alluvium).

Accompanying these climatic fluctuations in the Quaternary were major oscillations of sea level. During the cold glacial (periglacial) phases sea level fell, and the Isle of Wight became part of the mainland, a hilly area attached to Hampshire and Dorset, with a coastline far out to the south-west. There were phases when Early Man was able to walk to and from Europe across a broad lowland that is now beneath the English Channel. During the milder interglacial (interperiglacial) phases the sea rose, sometimes exceeding its present level, so that beaches (marine gravels) formed around the Isle of Wight when the sea stood several metres higher. Patches of these are preserved in the north-east of the island.

Other Quaternary formations include coastal deposits such as modern beaches, salt marshes, and tidal sand and mud flats. The Quaternary deposits of the Isle of Wight are similar to those found in Hampshire, and across Southern England.

THE GEOLOGICAL SEQUENCE

The sequence of geological formations dating from the Cretaceous, Tertiary and Quaternary periods in the Isle of Wight (Table 2) will now be described, with reference to their mode of origin. Mention will be made of sites where each formation is well exposed, and to the extent of its outcrop in the Isle of Wight.

CRETACEOUS

Wealden Beds

The oldest rocks seen in the Isle of Wight are the Wessex Marls, which with the overlying Vectis Shales constitute the Wealden Beds, of Lower Cretaceous age. The Wessex Marls (previously known as the Wealden Marls) consists of red, purple, and green clays and marls with minor beds of sandstone, deposited in a freshwater environment of slowly subsiding flood-plains, shallow lakes and swamps in a broad basin that extended across what is now southern England. Rivers from surrounding low-lying land carried down clay and silt, with occasional sand and grit, to build up valley floors and deltas as the basin subsided. Sandstones formed as river channel deposits and clays were laid down on bordering flood-plains. As the rivers meandered on the aggrading flood-plains the channel sands became buried by muddy deposits to form an alternating series of sands and clays. Thus in the cliffs of Brighstone Bay (page 119) the Sudmoor Point Sandstone divides into six sandy horizons between Chilton Chine and Brook Chine, representing a series of sandy channel deposits in a meandering, aggrading river zone on a muddy flood plain at least 1.8 km wide[10]. The climate was seasonally wet and dry, and at times fallen trees and other vegetable debris were washed down by river floods and deposited in and around the lakes. Some of these formed dark lignite (brown coal) layers, rich in organic material, the most notable being the accumulation of logs known as the Pine Raft exposed off Hanover Point (page 121)[11]. Large reptiles, such as Iguanodon, roamed this landscape, and left footprints on the muddy shores. Buried and preserved by further sedimentation, some of these are now to be found in layers of mudstone recently exposed along the shores of Brook Bay and west of Hanover Point. The rocks also include local accumulations of bones of reptiles and fish and freshwater shells. Sedimentation roughly kept pace with subsidence as the alluvial deposits built upwards.

The overlying Vectis Shales (formerly the Wealden Shales) consist of stratified dark grey, blue and black sediments with layers of sandstone and shelly limestone, and represents a change towards more brackish estuarine lagoons, with deepening water in the subsiding basin across Southern England. The rivers delivered mainly clay and silt, but sandstones formed where they brought down sand to build small deltas, or to be reworked by waves and shaped into beaches and barriers enclosing the lagoons. Thin limestones formed from shelly accumulations on lagoon floors. The associated fossils show that there were fish in the brackish water, as well as crocodiles and dinosaurs of various kinds. There are also the remains of ferns that grew beside the inflowing rivers.

On the Isle of Wight the Wealden Beds outcrop behind Sandown Bay, where they are much obscured by overlying alluvial deposits, and in the south-west, where they form a lowland a mile or so wide behind the cliffs that extend from Atherfield Point to Compton Bay. They typically form undulating lowlands with small woodlands and pastures on heavy, often wet, clay soils. The associated thin sandstones and limestones produce only minor landforms, as on the cliff-top at Barnes High, where a sandstone forms a small scarp (Fig. 6). They have been used locally in the walls of cottages and farm buildings, while the clays have been used for brick-making.

Fig. 6: The cliff-crest escarpment formed by the Barnes High Sandstone at Barnes High.

Deposition of the Wealden Beds came to end with a phase of slight uplift, followed by some erosion, which truncated the uppermost Vectis Shales, before the sea flooded back to deposit the overlying Lower Greensand.

27

Lower Greensand

The Greensand Beds were first named by the pioneer geologist William Smith in the eighteenth century from sandstone outcrops he observed in Wiltshire. The greenish tinge is due to the mineral glauconite (a silicate of iron, potassium and aluminium), which forms on submarine sand banks, and indicates a marine origin for these sandy sediments. It was only later realised that there were two Greensands, one above and one below the Gault clay, and these became known as the Upper and Lower Greensand. Moreover, Greensand exposures are usually green only at depth, in wells and borings, or in cliff exposures that remain saturated with groundwater: the iron compounds have often been oxidised near the surface to form red, brown, yellow or white sands.

The rise of sea level (known as the Aptian marine transgression) that submerged the slightly eroded Vectis Shales was accompanied by the deposition of the Perna Bed, about 1.5 metres thick, a green sandy clay overlain by brown calcareous sandstone. It can be seen rising westward from Atherfield Point through the cliffs of Brighstone Bay, and in a similar outcrop in the Yaverland cliffs, north-east of Sandown (p. 92). It was a shore deposit, rich in fossil shells, including one formerly known as Perna mulleti, from which it was named[12].

As the sea deepened, light brown and blue-grey silty clays were deposited over the Perna Bed. These became the Atherfield Clay, named from their exposure at Atherfield Point (Fig. 7). The accumulating sediment became sandier and more calcareous in the Crackers Bed, which has two hard layers, prominent in the cliff face east of Atherfield Point, where the name Crackers was given by Dr. W.H. Fitton from the splashing noise produced by waves breaking in cavities beneath them. There followed a long phase of sandy sedimentation in a relatively shallow sea, with brief intervals when silt and clay were deposited, producing the thick Ferruginous Sands[13]. Rich in ironstone (limonite) grains and iron oxide coatings, the Ferruginous Sands have weathered to red, yellow and brown at Red Cliff, east of Sandown; between Sandown and Knock Cliff; in Chale Bay between Rocken End and Blackgang (where the upper 30 metres of firm, coherent sandstones form vertical cliffs) and on to Atherfield Point; and in Compton Bay. Table 3 lists the subdivisions originally named by Dr. W.H. Fitton a century and a half ago[14] from the Chale Bay cliffs, at and west of Blackgang, as modified by the Geologists' Association[2]. These are still in use, although the nomenclature is clumsy and somewhat repetitive, and some of the subdivisions are difficult to distinguish in the cliff sections of Chale Bay (and are not recognisable in the cliffs of Ferruginous Sands elsewhere).

Sandy sediments continued to accumulate in the sea as the Ferruginous Sands were followed first by the paler (less ferruginous) sands of the Sandrock Series,

Above, Fig. 7: The sloping cliff at Atherfield Point, cut in crumbling Atherfield Clay.

Below, Table 3: Subdivisions of the Ferruginous Sands.

	SUBDIVISION	MAXIMUM THICKNESS
	Ferruginous Bands of Blackgang Chine	6.1 m
	Sands of Walpen Undercliff	30.5 m
	Foliated Clay and Sand	7.6 m
	Cliff End Sand	8.5 m
	Upper Gryphaea Beds	4.9 m
Ferruginous San	Walpen and Ladder Sands	12.8 m
	Upper Crioceras Beds	14.0 m
	Walpen Clay and Sand	17.4 m
	Lower Crioceras Beds	4.9 m
	Scaphites Beds	15.2 m
	Lower Gryphaea Beds	10.0 m
	The Crackers	18.3 m

as seen in the cliffs near Rocken End and at Knock Cliff, south of Shanklin, and then the coarser Carstone, again rich in iron oxides, weathered to dark brown in cliff exposures, as seen above Luccombe Bay, in Monk's Bay, at Blackgang and in Compton Bay.

The Lower Greensand outcrop extends from the cliffs of Blackgang and Chale Bay inland, narrowing westward along the southern side of the Central Downs to Compton Bay, but broadening eastward into the core of the Sandown Anticline, through to the coast between Shanklin and Culver Cliff. It forms undulating country, with minor escarpments on the harder parts of the Ferruginous Sands (particularly the Sands of Walpen Undercliff near the top of this formation), and on the Sandrock and Carstone. There are extensive lower areas on the softer underlying sands and clays around Atherfield and in the country behind Sandown and Shanklin. Some of the harder sandstones, particularly the dark brown Carstone, have been used in walls and buildings, as at Mottistone Manor and the nearby church.

Gault and Upper Greensand[15]

The dark brown Carstone is overlain by the Gault, typically a blue-black to greenish grey silty clay, rich in ammonites, deposited in a deepening sea (known as the Albian marine transgression). The Gault is a thin formation (generally less than 30 metres), and narrow outcrops are exposed in the cliffs of Compton Bay, between Blackgang and Luccombe, and on Culver Cliff. It is readily softened and weakened by groundwater seepage from the overlying Upper Greensand and Chalk, and has been responsible for major landslides on the coast, as well as inland along its outcrop below the Upper Greensand and Chalk escarpments.

The sea then became shallower, and the Gault clays were buried by the Passage Beds (sandy clays and marls) and then the glauconitic Upper Greensand, initially grey and green but weathering to pale yellow or orange sandstones, as in Culver Cliff and the cliffs of Compton Bay. Outcrops of steeply dipping Upper Greensand run from west to east through the Isle of Wight, and around the Southern Plateau, in front of the Chalk escarpment. They include the brown or bluish layered Chert Beds, formed by the segregation of siliceous material into harder horizons, as seen in the almost flat strata of Gore Cliff (Fig. 8).

Grey-green stone quarried from the Upper Greensand, notably the St. Boniface Stone from the Ventnor area, has been widely used in churches, houses, barns and walls in the Isle of Wight, particularly in Shanklin, Ventnor, St. Lawrence and Niton, and as far afield as Winchester Cathedral.

Fig. 8: Gore Cliff, with outcrops of the Chert Beds (Upper Greensand) capped by Lower Chalk. The scrubby foreground is an area that subsided over the Gault in a landslide in 1928.

Chalk

After the deposition of the Upper Greensand the sea deepened rapidly (this was the Cenomanian marine transgression) to at least 350 metres, and eventually perhaps more than 1,000 metres over much of Britain and France. As it did so the sandy Upper Greensand deposits were buried by calcareous marls including silt and clay derived from a nearby land area, producing the Grey Chalk and Chalk Marl divisions of the Lower Chalk. As the sea deepened further it became warm and clear, much like the Bahamas at the present time, and in what is now Southern England, then far from any land, the ocean shelf sediments became an almost pure calcareous sediment that eventually solidified into Chalk, a rather pure white limestone, which in the Isle of Wight is nearly 500 metres thick. This great thickness implies that the sea floor was steadily subsiding. Much of the Chalk is a friable (powdery) carbonate, with some shell fragments, and vast quantities of tiny spherical coccoliths (planktonic algae) deposited on the sea floor. Where these are concentrated the Chalk becomes hard and nodular.

Towards the end of Cretaceous times the Chalk was broadly uplifted and raised above the sea. The soft calcareous deposits dried and shrank, forming vertical cracks (known as joints) and emphasising the horizontal bedding planes that had marked pauses between the accretion of successive Chalk strata. There are only minor variations in the nature (lithology) of the Middle and Upper Chalk. There are a few hard blocky nodular horizons, notably the Chalk Rock near the top and the Melbourn Rock at a higher level in the Middle Chalk[16]. Siliceous material that had been scattered through the Middle and Upper Chalk (e.g. in fossil sponges) was dissolved by percolating water and became precipitated in nodules and layers of black flint, mostly along the bedding planes (i.e. between successive chalk layers), particularly in the Upper Chalk, which is thick, firm and well stratified.

Subdivisions of the Chalk can be determined with reference to particular fossils, which have been used to define a dozen palaeontological zones, but as these are not related to scenic features they will not be detailed here[17]. However, the palaeontological zonation shows that the highest horizons in the Chalk are seen on the southern side of Alum Bay (there are higher divisions in Norfolk and Denmark) and that the reduction in thickness of the Chalk from about 497 metres on the southern side of Alum Bay in the west to 430 metres south of Whitecliff Bay in the east is due to the greater subsequent truncation of the Upper Chalk by pre-Tertiary erosion in that direction.

The Chalk outcrops along the Central Downs and more broadly in the Southern Plateau. It typically forms smooth, rolling grassy downland with some cultivated areas on gentler slopes (Fig. 9). It reaches the coast only in the cliffs at the eastern and western extremities of the Isle of Wight, at Culver Cliff and alongside the ridge extending to The Needles. The Lower Chalk outcrop is marked by many former pits, from which lime and marl were taken for use on farmland in the clay country north and south of the Central Downs, and these are now seen as grassy hollows in the fields. The Middle and Upper Chalk form steep slopes on escarpments and valley sides.

Some of the hard bands in the Chalk, as well as flints, have been used locally in stone walls, farm buildings and cottages in the Isle of Wight. Flints were used by early Man, shaped into the implements found in Pleistocene gravel deposits.

Fig. 9: Coombes in the Chalk country above Gatcombe, looking north-east towards Newport.

THE END OF THE CRETACEOUS

At the end of the Mesozoic era, when the Chalk emerged from the Cretaceous Sea, the Isle of Wight became a land area. In the succeeding Palaeocene period (about 10 million years) erosion began to remove some of the higher zones of the Chalk, then sedimentation resumed in the Isle of Wight area as the sea rose again, submerging the surface of the Chalk. This marked the beginning of the Tertiary era.

There had been a major change in fauna and flora by the time these Lower Tertiary sediments began to accumulate. The menagerie of reptiles that had long dominated the world (including the dinosaurs that had roamed on land in the Cretaceous period) vanished, and the mammals (which had first appeared in the Triassic but stayed few in numbers and varieties), began to multiply, diversifying towards modern species. Ammonites, which had swarmed in the Cretaceous seas, also disappeared, together with the belemnites, but molluscs began to increase and diversify.

There were also major changes in the plant world. The land surface, which had previously been almost bare of vegetation, acquired a cover of trees, ferns and flowering plants. Grasses appeared, providing an ecological niche for the evolving hoofed mammals. In the Isle of Wight area the climate was warm and humid, and the countryside began to take on a modern aspect, the desert-like landscapes of earlier geological periods giving way to forested and grassy hills and valleys.

LOWER TERTIARY

Post-Cretaceous time (the Cainozoic Epoch) is divided into a long Tertiary Period with five Systems (Palaeocene to Pliocene), followed by a shorter Quaternary Period (Table 1). In the Isle of Wight the Lower Tertiary (sometimes known as the Palaeogene, comprising the Palaeocene, Eocene and Oligocene) formations are well represented, but Upper Tertiary (or Neogene) deposits are missing. During the Lower Tertiary the region that is now the Hampshire Basin and the Isle of Wight was receiving sediments ranging from gravel and sand to silt and clay from rivers draining a land area of moderate relief to the west and north-west. These were deposited on coastal plains and deltas, in estuaries and lagoons and in shallow seas that oscillated in level. At each horizon it is possible to trace, from Dorset in the west to the Isle of Wight in the east, a transition from generally coarse sediments deposited on land laterally to finer estuarine and deltaic sediments and then marine deposits, and as the sea rose and fell this sequence of sedimentary zones migrated landward (westward) and seaward (eastward).

The Lower Tertiary formations in the synclinal Hampshire Basin are similar to those in the London and Paris Basins to the north and south. They are remnants of once continuous Lower Tertiary strata deposited across the whole of southern Britain and northern France, and later folded into anticlines and synclines, with axes running west to east, by Miocene tectonic movements. The Tertiary deposits have been since removed by erosion from the intervening anticlinal area that extends from the Weald westward through Salisbury Plain, but they persist in the synclinal London and Hampshire basins, and in the northern half of the Isle of Wight they occupy the southern part of a broad and deep furrow in the Chalk that runs eastward from the Frome valley in Dorset and passes beneath the Solent and Spithead out to the south of the Sussex coast.

Deposits of Palaeocene age, overlying the Chalk, were originally described and named in the Thames valley[18]. In the Isle of Wight they are represented by the Reading Beds, the contact with the Chalk being seen in the cliffs of Whitecliff Bay and Alum Bay. These are followed by the Eocene deposits, comprising the London Clay, the predominantly sandy Bagshot Beds, the similar Bracklesham Beds and the Barton Clay and Barton Sand forming outcrops to the north. Then come the Oligocene Headon Beds, Osborne Beds, Bembridge Limestone and Bembridge Clay, and finally the Hamstead Beds in the northern part of the island. Each of these formations includes sediments carried by rivers ancestral to the Dorset Frome and Stour eastward into estuaries, lagoons and a shallow sea. The Lower Tertiary sediments show evidence of several cycles, indicating successive marine transgressions and regressions. Each cycle begins with fine sediments, clayey silts or silty clays, coarsening upwards to fine, medium and sometimes coarse sands[19].

PALAEOCENE

Reading Beds

At the base of the Reading Beds there is about a metre of coarse iron-stained marine sand with flint cobbles and pebbles resting upon the Upper Chalk. The sea that deposited these sediments advanced across an almost flat surface that had been cut into the Upper Chalk, reworking its superficial flint gravels and bringing in sands. The marine incursion was brief, for the thin sandy beds were soon buried by freshwater sediments, mottled red and purple clays deposited by rivers in shallow lakes. There were phases when these sediments emerged locally, long enough for soils and vegetation to form on them, the reddening of iron compounds showing that the climate was dry and probably warm. These soils were then submerged and buried by further clay deposition, forming palaeosols (ancient or fossil soils)[20].

Between Alum Bay and Whitecliff Bay the Reading Beds dip steeply northward (75°-80°) and form a narrow outcrop along the edge of the Upper Chalk slope of the Central Downs.

EOCENE

Oldhaven Beds and London Clay

At the beginning of the Eocene the freshwater clays of the Reading Beds were submerged by the sea, and there was deposition of about 4 metres of dark green loamy sand, equivalent to the Oldhaven Beds in East Kent[21]. There followed a series of minor oscillations of sea level as inflowing rivers laid down the London Clay, deposits of clay, silt and sand with occasionally pebble layers. The inflowing rivers had a gentle gradient, carrying mainly fine sediment derived probably from Jurassic outcrops exposed to the north and west, in what is now Dorset and Somerset.

The London Clay in the cliffs of Alum Bay and Whitecliff Bay is partly concealed by landslides, but the generally narrow outcrop runs through the island, parallel to the Reading Beds on a gently declining slope strewn with flinty drift from the Central Downs.

Bagshot Beds

Deposition of the London Clay came to an end with the arrival of coarser deltaic sediment supplied by a large river flowing in from the west. These were the Bagshot Beds, named from their occurrence in the Bagshot area, in Surrey. The sediments were mainly quartz sands, probably derived from weathered granite in what is now the Dartmoor region. The sharp colour variations in these beds are related to their mineral content: the white sands are clean quartz, the pink, red and purple sands have quartz grains coated with varying concentrations of haematite, the brown and yellow have sand grains coated with limonite[22], the green contain the mineral glauconite (p.28), while the dark beds are rich in organic matter. The actual colours vary with grain size, the degree of weathering and oxidation of these associated minerals, and their concentrations.

There are also some seams of pipeclay, which settled in shallow pools on the subsiding delta. They contain plant remains which include tropical plants, showing that the climate was warm and wet. Pipeclay, so called because it was used in making tobacco pipes, is a kaolinite derived from the decomposed felspars of the Dartmoor and Cornish granites.

The steeply-dipping Bagshot Beds outcrop runs through the Isle of Wight from Alum Bay to Whitecliff Bay. It is generally narrow, but widens where the dip diminishes around Freshwater and Calbourne. There is no distinctive topographic feature, the land generally declining northward across the sandy outcrop, which is partly obscured by a thin capping of flinty drift.

Bracklesham Beds

After the deltaic sands of the Bagshot Beds had been deposited the sea spread across this region, and sands and clays washed in by rivers formed glauconitic sediments with many marine shells, the Bracklesham Beds. These were named from outcrops on the shores of Bracklesham Bay, on the western side of Selsey Bill in Sussex. There is evidence of minor oscillations of sea level, with sequences of coarser marine sediment passing upward into finer sands, silts and clays, and thin lignite layers formed from reedy vegetation and drifting plant material. Apart from these oscillations the sea remained shallow while over 170 metres of sediment accumulated, indicating either a gradual marine transgression or steady subsidence. The sandy sediments show variations in colour similar to those of the Bagshot Beds.

The British Geological Survey map combines the Bracklesham Beds with the Bagshot Beds in an outcrop running from west to east, north of the Central Downs.

Barton Beds

The Bracklesham Beds are capped by another sequence of marine clays and sandy clays with shelly fossils, the Barton Clay, followed by white and yellow sandy sediments, the Barton Sand, deposited as an overlying delta. These formations were named from outcrops in the cliffs at Barton-on-Sea, on the Hampshire coast. They are seen in the cliffs at the northern end of Alum Bay where the northward dip diminishes, and they outcrop around the base of Headon Hill. In the east of the Isle of Wight they occupy a similar position in the cliffs at the northern end of Whitecliff Bay. The Barton Beds have also been included in the outcrop of the Bagshot Beds on the British Geological Survey map.

The Palaeocene and Eocene sands and clays of the Isle of Wight show no distinctive topographic features, their outcrops forming a gentle northward slope in the foreground of the steeply rising Chalk, but they form gullied cliffs in Alum Bay and Whitecliff Bay.

OLIGOCENE

Headon Beds

Subdivisions of the Lower Oligocene Beds are shown in Table 4, based on information in the Geologists' Association Guide[2]. The deltaic Barton Sands subsided beneath brackish lagoons, in which rivers deposited thin layers of marl and clay, the Headon Beds. Rapid changes in salinity resulted in accumulations of various species of freshwater, estuarine and marine shells, some of which have become grey or cream-coloured limestones, such as the How Ledge Limestone which forms a shore reef in Colwell Bay, and the Hatherwood Limestone, seen in a cliff high on Headon Hill (p. 132).

Osborne Beds	Osborne Marls
	Fishbourne Beds
	Lacey's Farm Limestone
Headon Beds	Cliff End Marls
	Hatherwood Limestone
	Linstone Chine Beds
	Colwell Bay Beds
	How Ledge Limestone
	Totland Bay Beds

Table 4: Subdivisions of the Lower Oligocene.

The Headon Beds are sometimes classified as late Eocene rather than early Oligocene. They occupy much of Headon Hill, and are also exposed in the cliffs of Totland Bay and Colwell Bay. Their outcrop narrows inland, and is generally featureless, except to the south-west of Newbridge, where the Upper Chessell valley runs along it. In the northern part of Whitecliff Bay the Headon Beds are seen as a series of sandy clays.

Osborne Beds

The lagoons in which the Headon Beds were deposited became swamps in which the succeeding red and green clays and marls of the Osborne Beds accumulated. It was a subtropical environment, rather like the present coast of Louisiana, where turtles and alligators waded through muddy shallows and fish and shelly organisms were prolific. Carbonates from the shelly material produced occasional pale grey limestones, such as the Lacey's Farm Limestone, seen on the eastern side of Headon Hill (323861).

The Osborne Beds are exposed at Cliff End, in the north-west of the island, and in sectors of cliff between East Cowes and Ryde, notably at King's Quay and Binstead. In the north-east the lagoonal clays and marls were buried by a sandy river delta, forming the Nettlestone Grits and the St. Helens Sands, seen on the shore between Puckpool Point and Priory Bay. The intricacy of the contemporary environment is well illustrated in the cliffs east of Nettlestone Point, where the upper division of the Nettlestone Grits passes laterally into a hard marl and then a shelly limestone, a gradation indicating that at this stage the sandy delta was bordered by mudflats and a shelly lagoon[23].

The Headon and Osborne Beds are combined on the British Geological survey map, and grouped as the Headon Hill Formation in the Geologists' Association Guide. Apart from their cliff outcrops, which have been much affected by slumping, and small features related to outcrops of the limestones, they have little topographic expression. Blocks of Nettlestone Grits have been used in the construction of sea walls locally.

Bembridge Limestone

The sea then withdrew, and the brackish swamps and lagoons gave place to freshwater lakes in which shelly organisms thrived, producing the white Bembridge Limestone. Inwashing of fine sediment from rivers laid down a few thin layers of shale and marl. The limestone outcrops in distinctive landforms in the cliffs and shore ledges at Nodes Point and around Bembridge Foreland, and forms prominent shore platforms at Hamstead Ledges, in Thorness Bay and at Gurnard Ledge. Inland where the dip is steeply northward the limestone outcrops on the bluff north of Bembridge Airport, overlooking the Eastern Yar meadows, and a low ridge along Wall Lane, to the north of Brading station (608873). There is a low escarpment and wide dip-slope where the dip is relatively small (less than 10°), as in the country around Newbridge and south of Wellow (Excursion 12). The British Geological Survey map shows Bembridge Limestone outcropping near the top of the northern and eastern slopes of Headon Hill.

Bembridge Limestone has been quarried, notably at Binstead and Quarr, where it was used in the building of Quarr Abbey. It is found in many of the older buildings on the Isle of Wight, including Yarmouth Castle.

Bembridge Marls

The top of the Bembridge Limestone is often uneven, indicating that the lake deposits emerged, and were eroded, before the sea submerged them, bringing a bed of black oysters and other marine shells. This was followed by a return to a brackish lagoonal environment (similar to that of the Osborne Beds) in which the Bembridge Marls, up to 30 metres of mostly grey-green clays and marls, accumulated, together with inwashed driftwood. In the north-east of the island there was some sandy deposition in estuaries[24].

The Bembridge Marls are seen in the slumping Hamstead cliffs in the north-west of the island, and from Priory Bay round the Bembridge Foreland to the northern end of Whitecliff Bay, resting upon Bembridge Limestone. Inland they outcrop in the lowland running east from Yarmouth to Newbridge, continuing in a narrow strip to Brading, then forming the undulating country, dissected by stream valleys, that runs from Bembridge along the north coast to Cowes and westward to Newtown.

Hamstead Beds

The brackish lagoons in which the Bembridge Marls formed became freshwater lakes in which green clays and black organic sediments, the Hamstead Beds, were deposited. Sea level then rose again, the water became brackish and eventually marine, and there was deposition of clays of various colours, together with some loams, shales and shell beds. The Hamstead Beds are exposed in the slumping Bouldnor cliffs and on the eastern side of Thorness Bay, and outcrop over a wide area in the northern part of the island, almost surrounded by the Bembridge Marls and Bembridge Limestone. The uppermost deposits, with estuarine and marine fossils, are known as the Cranmore Beds, and are seen in the top of Bouldnor Cliff, where they weather to brown clays.

The landscape of the Hamstead Beds is an undulating lowland with gravel-capped hills and ridges between the several river valleys. There are many shallow hollows, formerly pits from which clay was excavated for use in the making of bricks, much used in the buildings of Isle of Wight towns, particularly Newport.

The Cranmore Beds are the youngest of the Lower Tertiary formations on the Isle of Wight, and are of Oligocene age. It is possible that further deposition occurred in late Oligocene and early Miocene times, but if so these sediments have been subsequently removed by erosion.

THE GEOLOGICAL STRUCTURE
OF THE ISLE OF WIGHT

The Cretaceous, Eocene and Oligocene formations seen in the Isle of Wight were all originally laid down more or less horizontally, but they are now seen dipping at various angles. They were disturbed during a major phase of folding and faulting that took place in Miocene times, when the Eocene and Oligocene sands and clays that had accumulated over the Chalk, together with the older Cretaceous rocks, were sharply folded along generally east to west axes (Fig. 2).

The Sandown Anticline runs westward from Sandown Bay, where it is asymmetrical with a steeply-dipping northward flank, diminishing south of Newport and almost fading out in the high Chalk country between Gatcombe and Calbourne. As it diminishes the Brighstone (formerly known as Brixton) Anticline develops to the south, running north-west, then west, off the coast between Atherfield Point and Freshwater Bay. This is also asymmetrical, with steep dips on the northward flank. Thus, although similar, the steeply-dipping Chalk and Eocene strata of Whitecliff Bay are on the northern flank of the Sandown Anticline, whereas those of Alum Bay are on the northern flank of the Brighstone Anticline, the broadening of their outcrops south-west of Newport, occurring where the northward dip diminishes and fades out.

In addition to the prominent Sandown and Brighstone Anticlines there are smaller, roughly parallel, flexures (Fig. 2). South of the Sandown Anticline is the shallow Lake Syncline seen in the cliffs between Sandown and Shanklin (p. 94), followed by the Shanklin Anticline. To the north of the Central Downs the Bouldnor Syncline, bringing down the Hamstead Beds, the highest of the Oligocene formations, runs from the Bouldnor cliffs across the island to Bembridge Harbour. This is followed northward by the Porchfield Anticline, across which the Oligocene rocks rise and fall east from Newtown Harbour, and another small syncline which produces the change of coastal orientation from ENE to NNE in Thorness Bay.

The Miocene folding may have been associated with the movements that produced mountainous topography in Europe, notably the Alps. The asymmetry of the folding suggests that there was pressure from the south, but there may also been adaptations of the Cretaceous and Tertiary strata to the jostling of fault-bounded blocks in the underlying pre-Cretaceous formations. The top of the Upper Chalk (i.e. the base of the Palaeocene) stands almost vertical in Alum Bay and Whitecliff Bay, where it passes below present sea level, and declines to depths of more than 600 metres in the northern half of the Isle of Wight[25]. If the sub-Palaeocene surface is projected over the crest of the Sandown and Brighstone Anticlines it rises about 860 metres above present sea level, but it is unlikely that the ridge ever attained such an altitude, because the growing structure was undoubtedly eroded as the uplift proceeded.

When the folding came to an end the Isle of Wight was a land area undergoing denudation to expose the various geological structures and formations that have been described. While the Chalk and Lower Tertiary limestones were removed largely as carbonates dissolved in rivers and sea water, insoluble sediments such as clay (from the Weald Clay, the Gault and the London Clay), sand (from the Greensands and the Bagshot and Bracklesham Beds), and gravel (especially cherts and flints, recycled through successive geological periods) have been exported from this area since the Oligocene, carried away eastward and southward to be deposited on the floor of the English Channel[26]. Small proportions have been retained in sand flats, mud flats and salt marshes in the estuaries that open northward and eastward, and in the relatively sparse superficial deposits of Tertiary and Quaternary age, described below.

The Isle of Wight has been relatively stable since the Miocene folding came to an end, for the superficial deposits (see below) are horizontal, or only gently inclined. Earthquakes are rare, but there is evidence that gradual subsidence is continuing along the south coast of England[27].

SUPERFICIAL DEPOSITS

Angular Flint Gravel

Scattered across the Chalk uplands, generally between 130 and 230 metres above sea level, are patches of angular bleached and broken flint gravel. They are shown on the geological map where they are more than a metre, and locally up to 3 metres, thick, but thinner cappings are extensive. Chalk, like all limestones, consists largely of carbonates, dissolved by rain water, which is mildly acid because it contains carbon dioxide. Left behind is an insoluble residue consisting mainly of flint nodules, still angular in contrast with cobbles and pebbles that have become rounded as the result of abrasion in the course of transport by rivers or agitation by the waves of the sea.

The Chalk uplands have thus been lowered by solution: it has been estimated that at least 20 metres of Upper Chalk would have to be dissolved to produce a metre of flint gravel[28]. On the Central Downs these gravels rest upon the flinty Upper Chalk from which they have been derived, but in the Southern Plateau they overlie Middle and Lower Chalk, which contain few flints, and so they must either have been transported from Upper Chalk sources (possibly to the south, since removed) or lowered in situ from an Upper Chalk outcrop that has been dissolved away.

Some of this gravel formed under colder climatic conditions during the Pleistocene. As has been noted, there were several phases in Pleistocene times when ice sheets advanced southwards across Britain, at one stage reaching as far as the Thames valley. Climatic conditions in the Isle of Wight were then periglacial, similar to those now found in Arctic regions such as Greenland and Spitsbergen. The ground was repeatedly frozen and thawed, disturbing the Chalk surface, and many of the flints were broken by frost-shattering. Melting snow also contributed to rapid solution of the chalky matrix, and washed away some of the finer material.

Locally the angular flint gravel is accompanied by clay, probably derived from the overlying Reading Beds and London Clay, but Clay-with-flints of the kind seen on the Chalk uplands of Dorset and Hampshire[9] are not widespread on the Chalk of the Isle of Wight.   Where they do occur (in Brighstone Forest and on the Southern Plateau) they have a sharp but irregular contact with the underlying Chalk, locally extending down into hollows produced by solution, known as soil pipes, as seen in the cliffs on the eastern side of Freshwater Bay (p. 126).

It is difficult to assign an age to the angular flint gravel, for on the Central Downs it began to form when the Lower Tertiary formations had been removed to expose the Upper Chalk to subaerial weathering and erosion, probably in Pliocene times. It has continued to develop through the Pleistocene and the Holocene, and is still forming as each spell of rainfall dissolves away a little more chalk. On the Southern Plateau it is a relict deposit (not still being formed), and is probably of Pliocene and Pleistocene age.

Plateau Gravel

Deposits of mainly flint and chert gravel, with subangular and well-rounded cobbles and pebbles in an earthy matrix, are found on hill-tops and ridge crests north and south of the Central Downs, generally between 30 and 120 metres above sea level.   They are remnants of one or more extensive sheets of this material, spread across a land surface that has since been incised by rivers and dissected by valleys. As will be shown in the next chapter, this land surface includes terraces at several levels, and the Plateau Gravel may represent more than one stage of deposition during Pleistocene times. Some of the deposits contain flint implements shaped by Palaeolithic Man[29], who lived in this chilly Pleistocene Isle of Wight.

The Plateau Gravel on St. George's Down (514877) rests upon a surface about 100 metres above sea level, planed across steeply-dipping Chalk, Upper Greensand, Gault and Lower Greensand formations. The coarse pebbly gravels are several metres thick, partly stratified with sandy deposits and locally cemented by ironstone. Some of these deposits were carried by a river ancestral to the Medina, which is now incised into a valley to the west (page 149), but to be able to carry such a coarse load this Pleistocene river must have been much larger than the present Medina, and was probably fed by melting snow from former uplands to the south.

Other patches of Plateau Gravel, particularly those on ridges up to 8 kilometres north of the Central Downs, as at Cowes and above Osborne, and up to 4 kilometres from the Chalk escarpments, as near Apse (559833) and on Bleak Down (512815) include earthy rubble of the kind produced by sludging (solifluction) under conditions of repeated freezing and thawing, probably lubricated by melting snow (Fig. 10). They are similar to deposits that in Dorset and Hampshire have been mapped as Head or Rubble Drift[30]. They include flint, chert and sandstones of local derivation, and formed under cold climatic conditions, when they were derived from shattered outcrops of Chalk and Greensand and spread extensively northward and southward, even across gentle slopes.

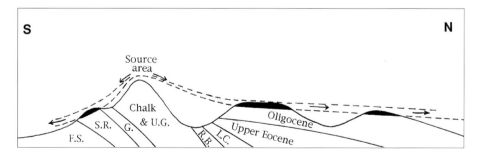

Fig. 10: Movement of flinty gravels derived from the Chalk northward and southward to form Plateau Gravel deposits (black) which have been dissected into hill cappings.

Thus Headon Hill (314858), 120 metres above sea level, is capped by angular flint and ironstone gravels in a sandy matrix, up to 8 metres thick (Fig. 11), which came from the Chalk and Eocene Beds to the south, carried by periglacial solifluction across a gentle northward slope which has since been excavated to produce a broad intervening valley to a depth of at least 60 metres[31].

Some of the Pleistocene gravels show contortions indicative of disturbance by alternations of freezing and thawing. These can be seen in partly overgrown gravel pits cut into the Plateau Gravel on Headon Hill. In places the leached sandy gravels are underlain by a dark brown layer of humate, consisting of downwashed organic matter with some precipitated iron oxides.

Fig. 11: The capping of Plateau Gravel over Osborne Beds on Headon Hill.

Marine Gravel

The Plateau Gravels 35-60 metres above present sea level in the north-east of the Isle of Wight, between Wootton and Bembridge, grade into deposits of well-rounded pebbles and sand which have been reworked by wave action when the sea stood at a higher level. There is also a deposit of beach gravels at Bembridge Foreland, extending up to 15 metres above present sea level, which is thought to date from a Late Pleistocene stage when the climate was warmer than it is now, and sea level a few metres higher. The implications will be discussed in the next chapter.

River Deposits

Other superficial deposits found in the Isle of Wight include river gravels, typically well-rounded pebbles in a sandy matrix, found on terraces (i.e. former valley floors, now dissected by incised rivers) bordering river valleys. River gravels can be seen on terraces beside the Medina valley at 70-80 metres on Shide Hill (507880), and at 20-25 metres bordering the Eastern Yar valley south of Arreton, as near Horringford Farm (544854).

Similar gravels occur beneath the present valley floors, laid down by rivers after they had cut valleys down to lower levels during Late Pleistocene times, and now concealed by finer flood-plain alluvium. These gravels indicate a phase when the landscape was poorly vegetated and coarse weathered material was swept down into valleys by heavy rain and melting snow. These gravelly Late Pleistocene deposits are overlain by Holocene alluvial deposits of finer sand, silt and clay, added during an ensuing phase of milder and moister climate, which sustained a vegetation cover and so limited sediment yields to fine-grained material carried by rainwash and rivers.

In the Chalk country the Pleistocene periglacial deposits include Coombe Rock, a chalky rubble found on the lower slopes and floors of dry valleys. It is well exposed in the cliffs of Freshwater Bay (347857) and Watcombe Bay (343856), where the frost-shattered chalk has moved down slopes, probably washed by melting snow, to form rubble lining the Western Yar valley (p. 135). There is no doubt that the dry valleys within the Chalk of the Central Downs and Southern Plateau have similar linings, formed during the late Pleistocene, and overlain by thin Holocene silty deposits carried down by rainwash.

Brickearth

Locally there are superficial deposits of structureless yellow, brown or grey loamy material known as Brickearth. These are seen banked up over the marine gravels of the Bembridge Raised Beach, and at intervals along the cliffs cut in the Wealden Beds and Lower Greensand on the south-west coast. In south-east England Brickearth originated as wind-blown sediment, a form of loess derived from the glacial drift deposits relinquished by retreating glaciers in the London Basin and on the floor of what is now the North Sea. Under cold conditions these deposits had little vegetation cover, and strong winds winnowed fine-grained silt and clay, and deposited them across land areas south of the former ice limit, including the Sussex and Hampshire coastal plains. Deposition probably occurred during the Last Glacial phase of the Pleistocene, between 25,000 and 50,000 years ago.

On the Isle of Wight Brickearth probably originated at this stage under periglacial conditions when the wind collected sediment from sparsely vegetated outcrops of unconsolidated sand, silt and clay formations. It is likely that much of the island became covered with a thin mantle of wind-blown sediment, part of which has been incorporated in the soil, or washed off hillsides to be added to slope-foot and valley-floor deposits.

Holocene Deposits

Deposits of black freshwater peat are found in the Wilderness, in the upper Medina valley, and along its tributary the Blackwater (515854). These are accumulations of rotting vegetable matter generated by swamp vegetation on poorly-drained flood plains. Estuarine peat has been formed on salt marshes in the estuaries of the Western Yar, Newtown Harbour, the Medina and Wootton Creek.

Slope-foot deposits include colluvium, an apron of rainwash and sediment carried down by soil creep, usually sand, silt and clay, and relinquished as the gradient diminishes. Similar material brought down from headwater regions has been distributed as alluvium across valley floors by recurrent river floods. Such deposits were generated when the post-periglacial vegetation cover was disrupted and cleared for agriculture, especially the ploughing of fields, in and after the Neolithic period, and successive episodes of slopewash may be correlated with changes in agricultural practice through Roman and Mediaeval times to the modern era of mechanised farming. An example of a Holocene slopewash deposit was found above Gore Cliff, near Niton, where molluscan shells derived from higher ground to the south (land that has since subsided into the Undercliff east of Blackgang [32]) were thought to have accumulated about 1800 years ago[33].

Sand dunes have formed behind beaches on the spits at Newtown Harbour and at the Duver, bordering Bembridge Harbour. Hummocks of wind-blown sand can be seen at the top of Ladder Chine, scoured from the Walpen and Ladder Sands outcrop in the cliffs by strong onshore winds, but the more extensive sheet of fine sand and silt capping gravel deposits on the crests of cliffs behind Chale Bay, extending horizontally at least 250 metres inland along the sides of Whale Chine (see cover photograph), lacks dune topography, and is probably a late Pleistocene Brickearth, winnowed from nearby outcrops of the Ferruginous Sands.

Landscapes of the Past

Although several of the geological formations in the Isle of Wight are of marine origin, deposited when the area lay beneath the sea, some contain evidence of past landscapes, in the form of terrestrial deposits and fossils (including the roots of ancient plants) and weathering features. Thus the early Cretaceous landscape, when the Vectis Shales were being deposited, was one with wide meandering sandy rivers on muddy flood-plains. The Palaeocene Reading Beds include deposits laid down on subsiding plains which at times were dry enough for the formation of soils and land vegetation. Landscapes with deltas and swamps existed at several stages in the Eocene and Oligocene in the Isle of Wight. The strong folding in Miocene times formed a landscape with high ranges, which were worn down and planed off, and later dissected into terraces that mark stages in a succession of landscapes through Pliocene and Pleistocene to Holocene times.

In Pleistocene times there were episodes of very cold climate when the landscape was bleak, with little if any vegetation, and the Isle of Wight was surrounded by wide plains exposed as the sea ebbed. These lost landscapes, once extending across to France and out to a lowered Atlantic coastline, now lie submerged beneath the English Channel and the straits of Solent and Spithead.

In the Holocene the modern landscape took shape, with the sea rising to its present level and the features of the present coastline evolving. As the climate became mild and moist, the landscape acquired a soil mantle and a cover of forest and scrub which Neolithic Man was to begin clearing, introducing grazing animals and cultivating crops. The present landscape incorporates features that date from landscapes of the Iron Age, the Roman occupation, the Anglo-Saxon era, Norman times, and on to modern farming and forestry, with buildings, villages and towns, roads and railways. The present scenery of the Isle of Wight is thus the latest of a long series of contrasting, evolving landscapes, and changes, both natural (erosion and deposition) and artificial (development and conservation) are still taking place.

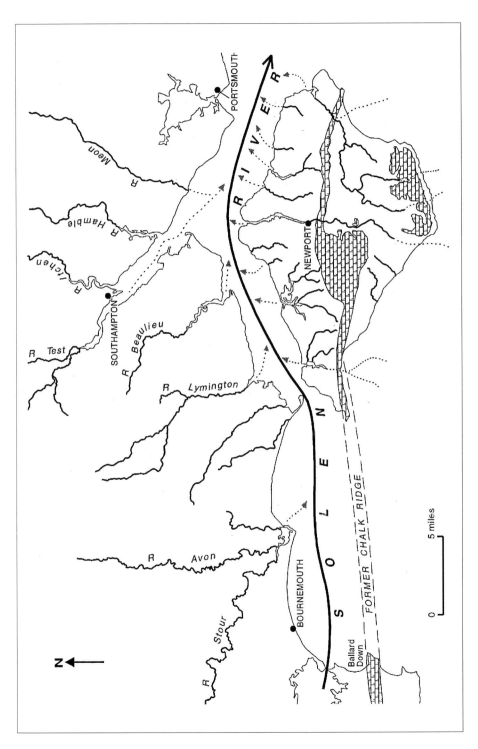

LANDFORM EVOLUTION

Introduction

The shaping of the Isle of Wight has been under discussion for well over a century. In 1862 the Reverend W. Fox, Vicar of Brighstone, addressed the question of when and how the island had been 'torn from the mainland and entrusted to the rude guardianship of the ocean'[34]. He realised that the Solent was 'to be accounted for not by excavation of a gradually approaching sea but by its being originally the trunk or outlet of a very considerable river, little inferior to the Thames or the Humber'. This was later to become known as the 'Solent River' (Fig. 12)[35]. Fox deduced that the Isle of Wight must then have been part of an elongated peninsula to the south of the valley of this river:

> Whoever as a geologist examines the vertical strata of the Chalk at the Needles, nay, and throughout the whole length of the Isle of Wight, and the stretch of the same rock in exactly the same unusual position on the bold white cliff on the Dorsetshire coast some twenty miles westward of the Needles, will not doubt but that the two promontories were once united, forming a rocky neck of land from Dorset to the Needles.

The Chalk ridge was in due course breached by the sea, and as the breach widened the Solent River estuary became a marine strait to the north of the Isle of Wight.

The more prominent features of the Isle of Wight, the hills and ridges inland, and headlands along the coast correspond with outcrops of relatively resistant geological formations, whereas valleys, lowlands and embayments have been excavated on softer outcrops. This had been recognised by Sir Charles Lyell in the first volume of his Principles of Geology in 1830[36]:

> We may point to the relation of the present shape and geological structure of the Isle of Wight, as attesting that it owes its present outline to the continued action of the sea. Through the middle of

Opposite, Fig. 12: The 'Solent River' and the former Chalk ridge that once linked the Isle of Wight to Ballard Down in Dorset.

the island a high ridge of chalk strata, in a vertical position, runs in a direction east and west. This chalk forms the projecting promontory of Culver Cliff in the east, and of the Needles in the west; while Sandown Bay on the one side and Compton Bay on the other, have been hollowed out of the softer sands and argillaceous strata, which are inferior to the chalk.

Some landforms coincide with the outcrop of a particular rock formation, such as the hard cherty Upper Greensand capping Gossard Hill (504841) west of Rookley, and forming an escarpment at Gat Cliff (534805). Chalk and sandstones also protrude because they are permeable, so that rainfall has percolated down through them instead of running off and washing away the surface to produce a more subdued outline. Geological structures, such as dipping rock formations, have also influenced the shapes of ridges and valleys in the landscape of the Isle of Wight: for example, the almost symmetrical ridge of steeply-dipping Chalk at the eastern and western ends of the Central Downs, and the gradual northward slope of gently dipping Bembridge Limestone south of Wellow (387882) (Excursion 12).

The geological structures that lie beneath the hills and valleys intersect the land surface to produce the pattern of outcrops seen on the geological maps, but the three-dimensional solid structure is more difficult to envisage. If one stands on, say, Bembridge Down, looking westward, it is possible to imagine the Chalk rising sharply from beneath the Lower Tertiary formations of the northern lowland to form the bold ridge of the Central Downs, and the underlying formations emerging to outcrop successively in ridges and valleys in the lowland to the south. The Chalk formerly curved over this lowland to join the Southern Plateau, where a large slab of it remains, truncated by the steep southern coast between Bonchurch and St. Catherine's Point. The removal of part of the Chalk cover has exposed the underlying formations, which have been dissected into the present ridges and valleys. The sequence of evolution, first of the rock structures, and then of the present scenery, can thus be deduced[37].

The Upland Plain

Evolution of the present landscape of the Isle of Wight began in Miocene times, with the uplift and folding of the Cretaceous and Lower Tertiary rock formations. This created a high topography, but erosion was in progress even when the folding and uplift were taking place, and eventually the structures were planed off (planation). The highest points in the present landscape, between 200 and 250 metres above sea level, are thought to be remnants of an upland plain, an ancient land surface cut across the folded structures in late Miocene to early

Pliocene times, and then uplifted and dissected by river valleys.

There is widespread evidence of such planation in Southern England, where most of the highest hill-tops stand between 200 and 250 metres, and very few exceed 300 metres above sea level. In the Isle of Wight they include the highest parts of the Central Downs, notably Brighstone Down (214 metres), and several summits above 200 metres in the Southern Plateau, including St. Catherine's Hill (236 metres) and a group north of Ventnor, culminating in St. Boniface Down (244 metres)[38].

Planation evidently occurred during a period when the sea stood about 200 metres higher, relative to the land, than it does now. The upland plain may have been cut by the sea when it stood at this higher level[39], but there is no evidence of any associated marine deposits. An alternative is that the land was worn down by subaerial processes (i.e. erosion by rainfall, runoff and rivers) to a peneplain (i.e. an almost flat plain). However formed, this plain has been subsequently raised by a fairly uniform tectonic uplift (or a substantial fall in sea level), so that the rivers began to incise valleys that dissected the various structures and formations to produce the existing topography, leaving only a few scattered hill-top remnants of the former upland plain[40].

The Pliocene Sea

It has been suggested that the Mio-Pliocene upland plain, now 200 to 250 metres above sea level in south-east England, was marginally submerged by a Pliocene sea, which cut a platform about 180 to 200 metres above present sea level, also bevelling local geological structures. Remains of this platform have been reported from the upper parts of Cranborne Chase in Dorset, from Salisbury Plain and from the Chalk uplands around the Weald of Kent, Sussex and Surrey[41]. In the Isle of Wight the highest parts of the Central Downs and the Southern Plateau are thought to have been islands in this Pliocene sea, which planed off the surrounding Chalk uplands. An extensive remnant of the Pliocene platform is seen on Chillerton Down at 165-170 metres. Although there are no confirmatory marine deposits in the Isle of Wight, a correlation has been made with a similar platform about 180 metres above sea level on the Kentish North Downs, which bears sandy shore sediments (the Lenham Beds) containing marine fossils of Pliocene age[42].

Evidence of early stages in the evolution of the landscape of the Isle of Wight is thus scanty, but it seems reasonable to accept that a Mio-Pliocene summit plain was formed, then marginally trimmed by a Pliocene sea. Ensuing uplift (or sea level lowering) established northward-flowing rivers across the emerging late Pliocene sea floor, and these became incised across the geological structures, cutting out valleys.

River Valleys and Drainage Divides

Rainfall and runoff in the Isle of Wight have supplied several river systems, each of which has excavated a basin consisting of valleys that converge and descend to present sea level (Fig. 13). Between the drainage basins are divides (watersheds) where the ground remains relatively high, even on soft rock formations such as the Gault on St. George's Down (page 149). The major divide between north-flowing and south-flowing rivers runs from The Needles along the Central Downs past Freshwater Bay to Brook Down, where there is a southward detour to the Lower Greensand ridge, then on the Brighstone Down. Thereafter it swings south-eastward to follow the breakaway behind the Undercliff, and descend to the coast at Sandown.

As Fig. 14 shows, the Medina, the Eastern and Western Yar, and a few smaller north-flowing streams and their tributaries drain a large proportion of the Isle of Wight. They run transverse to the generally east-west outcrops of rock formations, and several have cut gaps through the Chalk ridge of the Central Downs: the Western Yar, the Chessell stream, the Medina and its tributary Lukely Brook, the Eastern Yar and its tributary the Yaverland stream. The low sector north of Shorwell may also have been initiated by a northward-flowing transverse stream (Lukely Brook), but this was shortened as Yafford Brook excavated the soft Wealden and Lower Greensand to the south and grew headward through the Upper Greensand to the Chalk, reversing the drainage at Shorwell. More generally, rapid excavation of relatively soft formations north and south of the Chalk and Upper Greensand left the Central Downs upstanding as a steep-sided ridge.

The Eastern Yar has excavated a wide basin in the soft Gault clay, Lower Greensand and Wealden Beds to the south of the Central Downs, and tributaries of the Newtown, Medina and Wootton Creek systems have cut down into the broad outcrop of the Hamstead Beds to the north.

A few of the tributaries of north-flowing rivers have become adjusted to structure in the sense that they flow along outcrops that run parallel to the east-west axes of folding. Examples of this are Clamerkin Brook, flowing along the southern flank of the Porchfield Anticline and the Brook stream, flowing along the northern side of the Brighstone Anticline.

The major divides also show little relationship with the geological structure, outcrops of the various formations running across them. The uplands of Chalk and Upper Greensand are nevertheless areas from which many headstreams rise (Fig. 14).

Coastline recession has removed extensive areas formerly drained by

Opposite: Fig. 13: Drainage basins.

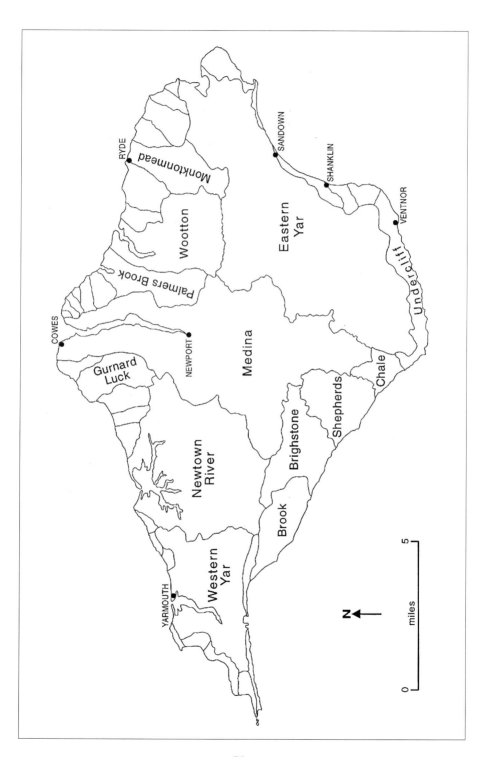

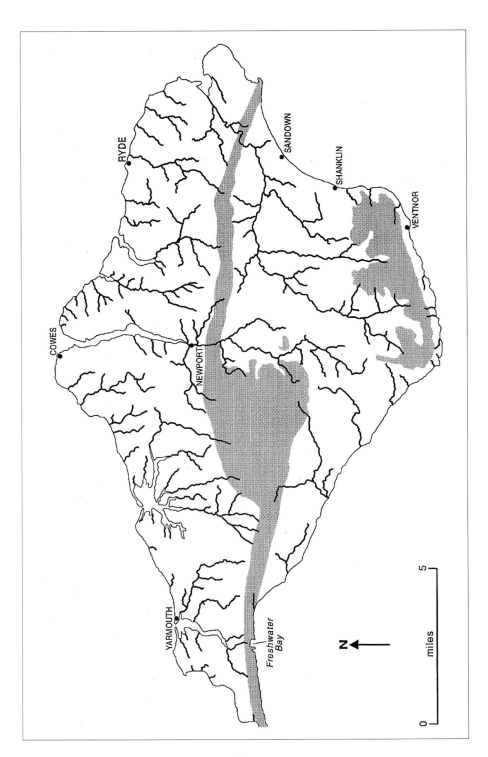

RYDE

SANDOWN

SHANKLIN

VENTNOR

COWES

NEWPORT

YARMOUTH

Freshwater
Bay

N

0   5

miles

headwaters of the Eastern and Western Yar on uplands that existed south of the island. The Western Yar has been beheaded, and is now only a small stream flowing through a wide valley cut when it was a much larger river. Gravels capping the cliffs of Brighstone Bay are inheritances from former westward-flowing tributaries of the upper Western Yar, of which the Brook stream is a minor remnant.

The drainage pattern has also been modified locally by river capture. Near Merstone, for example, there is a broad low watershed (528843) where the Eastern Yar has intercepted some former headstreams of the Blackwater, a Medina tributary. Thus beheaded, the Blackwater is now only a small stream flowing through the wide valley that was cut before the diversion took place. Like the Western Yar, it is an example of an 'underfit' river. The Eastern Yar, having acquired headstreams that drain the country around Godshill, turns eastward at Horringford (540854) to run along the strike of the Ferruginous Sands outcrop, close to the axis of the Sandown Anticline, and then north-eastward through the Brading Gap to reach the sea at Bembridge.

Around the coast there are a number of small drainage basins (Fig. 13) with short streams flowing down to the sea. Some of these have cut narrow, steep-sided ravines, known as chines, that open through a cliffed coast. Stream incision has been intensified because the stream mouths have been repeatedly lowered as the cliffs are cut back. A local example of stream diversion occurred when Atherfield Brook, which used to flow to the sea by way of Cowleaze Chine, was intercepted by the headward growth of Shepherd's Chine (p. 116).

Many of the valleys, especially headwater valleys cut into Chalk or the Upper or Lower Greensand, are now dry valleys or coombes (Fig. 9), with only brief and intermittent stream flow when the groundwater table is raised by prolonged rainfall or the melting of winter snow. In general, erosion by runoff and streams is now very slow, but there are occasional episodes of flooding, particularly in the Eastern Yar.

Stages in Landscape Evolution

The excavation of geological formations by rivers and the formation of valleys and drainage basins took place in several stages, indicated by a series of terraces related to formerly higher sea levels. As noted in the previous chapter, many of these bear deposits that were laid down by rivers or by the sea.

There is no doubt that the sea formerly stood at higher levels in southern England, even if it is difficult to confirm that it reached as high as 180 to 200 metres in the Pliocene. In Hampshire the evidence becomes stronger at lower

Opposite: Fig. 14: River systems. The shaded area is the outcrop of the Chalk and Upper Greensand.

levels, where C.E. Everard found terraces at various levels from 145 down to about 4 metres above present sea level[43]. On the Isle of Wight he found beach cobbles mixed with angular flints at 125 metres on Mersley Down (558874), and equivalent features on the summit at 130 metres (585869) and at 128 metres on Nunwell Down (559873). These he correlated with a stage when the sea stood about 130 metres above its present level, widely in evidence in Hampshire. There are also marine gravels on hill-tops about 35-60 metres above sea level in the north-east of the Isle of Wight, on the dissected remnants of a terrace that rose to a former coastline extending from Great Thorness east-south-east to St. Helens.

The most obvious evidence of a higher sea level is the Bembridge Raised Beach. This contains wave-deposited shingle (mainly flint and chert, with some sandstone and quartzite), resting on a platform cut in Bembridge Marls and rising south-westward to the base of a buried cliff about 15 metres above present mean sea level[44]. The inner part is blanketed with Brickearth up to 10 metres thick, so that the terrace surface rises to more than 25 metres above sea level. The Geological Survey map shows equivalent patches of marine gravel on the St. Helens plateau to the north, on the Pondwell spur, the Elmfield plateau, the plateau in the south-western suburbs of Ryde, on the Binstead ridge and capping Quarr Hill, all about 10-15 metres above sea level. These features are probably equivalent to the Portland Raised Beach in Dorset, and to several other Pleistocene raised beaches along the south coast of England, as at Goodwood and Black Rock in Sussex, Hopes Nose near Torquay, Hallsands near Start Point, and in South Cornwall. These are all considered to be of Last Interglacial (Ipswichian) age, because the ancient beaches are overlain by superficial deposits of periglacial origin, formed during the succeeding Last Glacial (Devensian) stage. This Last Interglacial coastline must have extended all round the Isle of Wight, but most of it has been destroyed by subsequent marine erosion: it survives only in the relatively sheltered north-east.

Supporting evidence of successive stages of higher sea level comes from the river terraces, usually with a mantle of fluvial gravel, sands and silts. These descend in level downstream, and are the dissected remnants of earlier valley floors formed when the river flowed to a higher sea level. The present valley floors also descend in level downstream, and have a covering of alluvial deposits comprising sediment brought down by the river from the headwater regions and spread across the valley floor by occasional floods.

The present valley floor of the Medina, for example, descends from more than 60 metres above sea level near Chale Green to about 1.2 metres (i.e. high spring tide level) at Newport Quay (Fig. 15). There appears to be a steepening near Champion Farm (about 499851), downstream from which the valley is slightly incised, remnants of its former floor persisting as a low terrace, such as

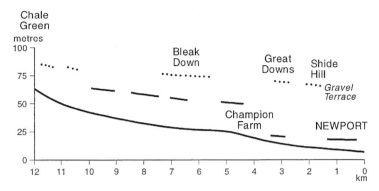

Above, Fig 15: The profile of the valley floor of the Medina River above Newport, with terraces thought to be remnants of similar earlier valley floors.

Above, Fig 16: A view across the incised Upper Medina valley near Rookley.

Below, Fig 17: Terracettes on the Upper Greensand slope at Gat Cliff.

the one on which much of Newport has been built. This is a Late Pleistocene terrace, descending to a sea level 5-10 metres higher than at present. There are also remnants of earlier valley floors at higher levels, a middle terrace descending to about 40 metres and a high terrace, bearing Plateau Gravel, descending to about 65 metres (Fig. 16). As previously noted (p. 43), the gravels on St. George's Down may represent a still earlier stage, about 100 metres above present sea level.

There are similar river terraces on both sides of the alluvial valley floor of the Western Yar, standing about 3 metres above the present valley floor. In the middle part of the Eastern Yar valley, where the river flows across a wide lowland on the Lower Greensand, the highest terraces are capped with Plateau Gravel, as on Frog Hill (547823), near Sandford, at 60-65 metres, with equivalents at Branstone Cross (559834) and Winford (566835), to the north, a few metres lower. These are remnants of an earlier, wider valley floor strewn with flint and chert pebbles from the Chalk and Upper Greensand to the south, and descending to a former coastline between 50 and 60 metres above present sea level. This was incised by the Eastern Yar and its tributaries, which then developed another valley floor which descends from about 60 metres on either side of the valley north of Whitwell to 20-30 metres on the wide gravel-capped terraces south of Arreton and on Hale Common (544844), and thence probably to the 15 metre coastline represented by the Bembridge Raised Beach.

The present alluvial valley floor of the Eastern Yar stands about 50 metres above sea level near Whitwell, descends to 15 metres north of Godshill, and then declines gradually to about 1 metre as it passes through the Brading Gap, where it widens into the reclaimed meadows towards high tide level in Bembridge Harbour.

Much more study is needed to define and correlate these river terraces, and to establish their relationships with former higher sea levels. The present valley floors are underlain by deeper channels, cut when sea level was lower in late Pleistocene times. During the Late Quaternary marine transgression the valley mouths were submerged to form Newtown Harbour, the Medina estuary, and the other estuarine inlets on the north and east coast of the Isle of Wight. There was then infilling with alluvial sediments to form the existing flood-plains.

There has been much artificial modification of river channels and valley floor topography by the addition of banks and the cutting of drains, especially in the Eastern Yar valley. The swampy section of the Upper Medina valley above Cridmore (503823), known as The Wilderness (495814), shows peaty aggradation which may be partly due to the construction of embankments across the valley floor, impeding runoff[45].

Slopes

Apart from the coastal cliffs, slopes in the Isle of Wight have developed as the result of subaerial processes, leading to the cutting and widening of river valleys and the recession of escarpments developed on outcrops of the more resistant (or more permeable) rock formations. There are steep slopes where the river has undercut the valley side, as along the Eastern Yar valley between Horringford and Bragg's Hill (583857), east of Alverstone, and on the southern side of the reclaimed flood-plain east of Brading (p. 78).

Runoff after heavy rain washes sediment down valley sides, but on these vegetated slopes most of the erosion takes place as a result of wastage by 'soil creep', the gradual down-slope movement of soil and superficial weathered material. Locally on steep slopes this has been shaped into terracettes, (small horizontal ledges about 30-40 cm wide), formed by cattle or sheep trampling. These can be seen on steep slopes in the Upper Greensand, as on Gat Cliff (Fig. 17), and on the Chalk, where they have formed very recently on the slopes of abandoned quarries on the southern side of Chillerton Down (476834).

Slopes can also be undercut by groundwater seepage, leading to the washing out of sediment at their base, particularly where permeable rocks overlie an impermeable layer. Examples of this are seen in the Lower Greensand country, where steep slopes have formed on sandstones in the upper part of the Ferruginous Sands, overlying impermeable clays, as in the ridge that runs from South Down (477787), near Chale, northward to Kingston (479814) and in the Godshill area (Excursion 6). The same process has formed minor escarpments on thin sandstones underlain by shales or marls in the Wealden Beds, as at Barnes High (Fig. 6).

More dramatic movements (landslides) have occurred on escarpments, producing basal hummocky topography where masses of Chalk and Upper Greensand have slid down over the Gault. The British Geological Survey map indicates these on the western and northern slopes of the St. Catherine's Hill and Head Down (507778), at the northern end of Appuldurcombe Down (536797), and along the escarpment between St. Martin's Down and Luccombe. Landslides have also occurred in the Oligocene formations on the flanks of Headon Hill, and coastal landslides are discussed below.

Some of these landslides are still intermittently active, but most were formed during cold phases of the Pleistocene, when slope instability was increased by periglacial freeze-and-thaw alternations, accompanied by occasional runoff from melting snow, which weathered and lubricated rock outcrops, triggering down-slope mass movements.

The effects of Pleistocene periglacial processes on the slopes of the Isle of Wight may be deduced from the nature and distribution of the deposits produced under these colder conditions, as described in Chapter 2. The existence of remnants of thin but extensive sheets of periglacial rubble indicates that the source areas, especially the Chalk slopes, were eroding as the result of frost-shattering and slope wastage during successive cold phases. It is likely that these slopes were steepened and became cliffy outcrops of disintegrating rock, receding as frost-shattered material was carried away down to the lowlands. Some of the deep Chalk coombes (Fig. 9) were excavated under these conditions, leaving deposits of frost-shattered Coombe Rock at lower levels, as seen in the cliffs of Freshwater Bay (p. 126). In general, the periglacial legacy is seen in the steep slopes that form escarpments and border incised valleys, and in the spreads of angular gravel that cap hills and the higher terraces.

At the end of Pleistocene times the world's climate became milder, and in the Holocene[46] the Isle of Wight became well vegetated, with a soil cover forming on the weathered rock outcrops. Slope erosion then yielded only fine-grained sediment (sand, silt and clay), which was carried down by rainwash and creep, to be spread across valley floors as flood-plain alluvium.

COASTAL FEATURES

Changing sea levels

The coastal features of the Isle of Wight have been shaped in the course of the Quaternary oscillations of sea level mentioned in Chapter 2. The island became part of the mainland during phases of low sea level, while during high sea level episodes it became an island again, with the sea invading the mouths of its river valleys to form estuaries. About 18,000 years ago, during the Last Glacial phase of the Pleistocene, the sea fell some 140 metres below its present level. The English Channel was then a broad plain, and in Southern England the rivers of Dorset, Hampshire and the Isle of Wight incised the lower parts of their Late Pleistocene valleys, and extended their courses out across the emerged sea floor to join the 'Solent River' mentioned above (Fig. 12)[34]. This river system previously existed several times, during low sea level phases in the Tertiary and the Pleistocene, and was inundated by the sea to form the marine gulf deduced from evidence of former coastlines in the Hampshire Basin[43]. The breaching of the Chalk ridge to the south was accomplished in stages, partly by gaps cut by rivers and subaerial erosion in low sea level phases, and partly by marine penetration when sea level rose. The Solent River certainly existed during the Last Glacial low sea level phase of Pleistocene times, when gravels were deposited on what is now the floor of the Solent and Southampton Water[47].

At the end of Pleistocene times the world's climate became milder, and between 18,000 and about 6,000 years ago widespread melting of glaciers and ice sheets released large quantities of water to the oceans. The outcome was a world-wide sea level rise, known as the Late Quaternary marine transgression[48], which brought the sea up to approximately its present level. The Solent River valley was then finally invaded by the sea, and remaining parts of the Chalk ridge between Ballard Down and the Needles were submerged and planed off by the sea to form the existing 15 mile strait. Submergence of the lower parts of river valleys on the Isle of Wight formed estuarine inlets by drowning the channels that had been cut during the preceding low sea level phase. Newtown Harbour is one of these, a branching estuarine system, while Bembridge Harbour at the mouth of the Eastern Yar and Yarmouth Harbour at the mouth of the Western Yar also owe their origin to this submergence, culminating in Holocene times.

The past 6,000 years has been a period of stillstand, with sea level remaining relatively stable, apart from minor oscillations resulting mainly from the gradual subsidence of southern England[49]. The drowned valley mouths have been partially infilled with Holocene sediment brought down by the rivers and washed in from the sea to form depositional plains above high tide level, and extensive intertidal mudflats and salt marshes. Inlets such as Newtown Harbour have been reduced by Holocene deposition to form alluvial plains and areas of marshland, mudflat and shoals. Some intertidal and salt marsh areas have been artificially reclaimed for agriculture (as in the Eastern Yar valley below Brading).

Cliffs

As the Holocene sea rose to its present level the higher parts of the coast were cut back to form cliffs, the crests of which undulate across the truncated hills and valleys. Small rivers draining to steep coasts were truncated by cliff recession, and cut chines. Cliffed promontories (such as the Foreland) occur where harder rocks (such as the Bembridge Limestone) outcrop at sea level, while cliffs in coves and bays (such as Whitecliff Bay) have been excavated in softer outcrops (Palaeocene and Eocene sands and clays), particularly where these have already been lowered by stream erosion. In detail, lines of weakness such as joints and faults have been exploited to form clefts and caves, and locally to isolate stacks such as the Needles. Barriers of harder rock have been breached and bays excavated in softer backing formations, as at Freshwater Bay, cut into frost-shattered Chalk.

Cliff profiles are also related to varying rock resistance and permeability, so that the Chalk, Greensands and Bembridge Limestone all form bold outcrops: The Needles occur where the Upper Chalk has been hardened as the result of intensive folding. However, in addition to geological factors it is necessary to take account of the effects of weathering, rainwash and slumping, as in the Lower Tertiary formations in Whitecliff Bay and Alum Bay (Fig. 18). The cliffs of Palaeocene and Eocene formations, having been cut back by marine erosion, have been etched into an intricate topography, the slightly harder sandstones protruding as ribs while the softer silts and clays have been excavated as furrows, gullies or hollows (Fig. 18). It is interesting that the early Tertiary cycles of deposition (p. 35) in these rocks, which produced the alternations of fine (soft) to coarse (hard) sediment, are thus expressed in the modern cliff topography.

Fig. 18: Cliffs in steeply-dipping sands and clays in the Eocene formations in Alum Bay, looking south towards the Upper Chalk.

Coastal Landslides

Cliff recession has been accompanied by landslides of various kinds, which have generated a fine array of features on the coast of the Isle of Wight, particularly near Yaverland in Sandown Bay, between Luccombe and Rocken End, at Blackgang and along the coast to Compton Bay, between Headon Hill and Yarmouth, between Bouldnor and Hamstead, in Thorness Bay and Gurnard Bay, and locally along the north-east coast. Mass movements of rock, weathered material and soil from high to low ground have taken the form of sudden rockfalls or landslides over a clearly definable shear surface, either translational (down a plane) or rotational (over a concave curve). An example of a deep-seated rotational slide has been described from Horestone Point[50]. There have been several landslides here, and after each landslide there is a mass of back-tilted rock, dipping landward at 30°-40°, on the shore, which is gradually consumed by wave action.

On the south coast between St. Catherine's Point and Luccombe Bay masses of Chalk and Upper Greensand have disintegrated and subsided over the Gault clay to form the Undercliff (Fig. 19). It is likely that there was already a landslide topography here, similar to that seen along the escarpments to the north (page 157), produced under Pleistocene periglacial conditions, before the Holocene sea began to undercut the foot of the slope, causing further instability. An upper cliff of gravel-capped Upper Greensand and Lower Chalk, up to 70 metres high, overlooks an area up to 600 metres wide of irregular slopes where slumped, broken and tilted masses of Chalk and Upper Greensand have been moving down over the outcrops of the impermeable Gault clay, lubricated by seeping groundwater. A lower cliff, up to 40 metres high and receding as the result of basal marine attack, is cut in Lower Greensand formations, mainly the Carstone and Sandrock Beds, over which masses of slumping Chalk, Upper Greensand and Gault have been spilling down to the shore.

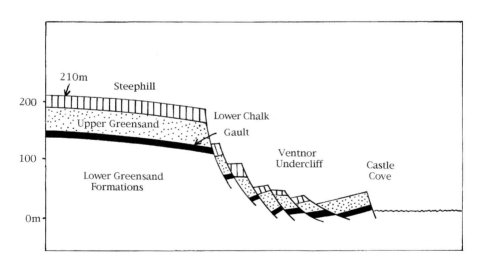

Fig. 19: The structure of the Ventnor Underrcliff, showing rotational subsidence of the Chalk and Upper Greensand over the Gault. Compare Figs. 49 and 50.

The Undercliff in the Ventnor district now appears relatively stable, but movements still occur, particularly during and after wet weather when groundwater seepage increases. There has been local subsidence on roads in the St. Lawrence area, and some buildings have been damaged by movements of their foundations[51]. There were major landslides between Luccombe Chine and Bonchurch in 1810 and 1818, and a large landslide west of Niton in 1928 removed part of the old Undercliff Road, and left tumbled masses of Chalk, Upper Greensand and Gault on an irregular slope, now partly vegetated, descending to Rocken End (Fig. 8).

On several sectors of the coast of Brighstone Bay, cliff recession has occurred behind basal ledges of harder or impermeable rock. Debris that has fallen from the cliff is washed across the basal ledge and down to the shore. At Blackgang there is a cliff about 100 metres high, cut in the Lower Greensand formations that overlie the Foliated Clay and Sand: the Sands of Walpen Undercliff up to the Sandrock Beds and the Carstone. The Undercliff is a terrace on Foliated Clay and Sand up to 130 metres wide, ending in a lower cliff 5-10 metres high.

There have been major changes here during the past century. Drawings made in the 1840s (Fig. 20) show a deep V-shaped valley with bordering ledges on the hard Ferruginous Bands of Blackgang Chine, about 6 metres of coherent brown and yellow sandstones over which a cascade spilled down to the shore. It was then possible to walk down this chine to the shore. However, since the first Ordnance Survey six-inch to the mile map was made in 1898 the upper cliff has been cut back about 275 metres, almost completely consuming the chine, while the lower cliff has receded about 30 metres. Recession of the upper cliff occurs as a result of seepage at the base, where groundwater emerges at the top of the Foliated Clay and Sand. Outwash by this seepage has been has been responsible for the undermining, collapse and recession of the high backing sandstone cliffs, and the consequent disappearance of Blackgang Chine. Undermined, the cliff face topples, slumps and disintegrates, and a combination of runoff and seepage sweeps fans of sandy material away across the undercliff terrace (Fig. 21). This is carried down over the lower cliff on to the beach, and dispersed by wave action[52]. The lower cliff is being cut back intermittently by waves at high tide.

Episodes of rapid cliff recession have occurred particularly after wet weather. At the beginning of March 1978 the melting of a heavy late winter snowfall saturated the sandstones, and cracks up to 3 metres wide opened behind the cliff top, a segment over 1,300 metres long then collapsing on to the Undercliff. Between 1978 and 1980 the upper cliff receded about 45 metres. Further such subsidence occurred in December 1993 and January 1994, when the sandstones were soaked by heavy rainfall, and at one point the cliff edge is now only just over 100 metres from the main Military Road.

On coastal outcrops of soft formations, especially clays and marls, mudslides,

Above: Fig. 20: Blackgang Chine, as it was in the 1840s, showing the Cascade over the Ferruginous Bands (from a sketch by W.H. Fitton[14]). Compare Fig. 54.

Below: Fig. 21: Aprons of downwashed sandy material and seepage fans on terrace of Foliated Clay and Sand in front of the Blackgang cliffs at the site of the former Blackgang Chine.

usually lobate and elongated, form and move slowly downslope, torn by shearing and tension cracks. These have been compared with glaciers, their cracks and slips opening and closing like ice crevasses as they subside, leaving behind arcuate cliff-backed corrie-like hollows. They are well developed on the coast near Bouldnor and Hamstead, where 'mud glaciers' have formed lobes protruding up to 30 metres into the sea[53]. More rapid movements, especially during very wet weather, include mudflows (where unconsolidated materials soaked with water move as a viscous mass), topples (where lumps of rock and soil break away and subside), and rock falls, (when detached material drops from a cliff and forms a scree of talus)[54].

Shore platforms

Shore platforms are cut by marine erosion as a cliffed coast recedes. They are poorly developed on clay outcrops and incoherent Tertiary sediments, or where cliffs in massive formations plunge below sea level, as on the Chalk near the Needles. Elsewhere, they take the form of structural ledges, as on the more resistant layers of the Bembridge Limestone and the sandstone horizons in the Wealden Beds, which form a ledge on the shore of Brighstone Bay between Chilton Chine and Hanover Point. Shore platforms cut across geological outcrops by marine abrasion (waves armed with sand and gravel) are found only locally and on a small scale, as on the coast fronting Chalk cliffs south of Whitecliff Bay (Fig. 22).

Beaches

The beaches of the Isle of Wight are generally of local derivation, consisting of sand and gravel produced by erosion of nearby cliffs and nearshore outcrops and distributed along the shore by wave action. Sandy beaches have been supplied with sand from sandstones in the Tertiary formations of Alum Bay and Whitecliff Bay, and from the Upper and Lower Greensand, particularly on the south-east coast between Sandown and Shanklin. In the vicinity of Chalk outcrops there are cobbles and pebbles of dark flint, sometimes with a white coating, freshly eroded from nodular horizons exposed in the cliffs and on the rocky foreshore. The Greensands have yielded similar brown chert pebbles. Some flint and chert shingle has been derived from cliff-top gravels, which have slumped down to the shore in Brighstone Bay (p. 120): initially angular, these slowly become well-rounded pebbles as the result of abrasion and attrition by waves breaking on the beach.

Some beaches include sand and gravel washed in from the sea floor, as is evident in the sandy deposits on beaches and foreshores in front of the clay and marl cliffs of Brighstone Bay. Below the landslides of the southern coast beach sands have come mainly from the Lower Greensand, partly from cliff erosion and longshore drifting, and partly from the sea floor[55]. On the north-east coast there are beaches dominated by locally-derived sandstone gravels, as at Nettlestone Point, or limestone gravels, as at Nodes Point. Very little beach material has come from the rivers, which have been delivering only fine-grained sediment (silt and clay) to their estuaries and the adjacent coast.

In general the predominance of wind and wave action from the south-west has caused beach material to drift eastward, as shown by the accretion of beaches

Fig. 22: Part of the shore platform cut across steeply dipping Upper Chalk strata on Whitecliff Point.

on the western sides of natural obstacles such as landslide lobes under St. Catherine's Point and man-made obstacles such as the breakwaters and groynes at and west of Shanklin Point. Beaches have been shaped by incident wave action, often with the coarser gravel piled up by swash as an upper beach and finer, sandy material withdrawn to the foreshore by backwash, and exposed at low tide, as at Sandown. Short-term changes occur in response to storm waves, which tend to carry beach material, especially sand, seaward, and gentler wave action in fine weather, which produces shoreward drifting, often in the form of a migrating sand berm.

The Changing Coastline

The effects of marine erosion and deposition have been to simplify coastal outlines, so that only the most resistant rocks persist as promontories, such as the Chalk and the Bembridge Limestone. The south-west coastline has become adjusted to fit the gently curved patterns of waves that move in from the English Channel. Between Blackgang and Compton Bay there are still minor promontories, such as Atherfield Point, where resistant rocks outcrop at the base of the cliff or close to the shore, but in Alum Bay and Whitecliff Bay the cliffed coastline cut in soft Palaeocene and Eocene rocks has become more open

Fig. 23: The former Arch Rock, Freshwater Bay, in 1991. It collapsed into the sea on 25th October 1992.

and smoothly curved.

Recent stages in the evolution of the coastline can be traced with reference to historical maps[56]. Various measurements of coastline change have been reported around the Isle of Wight. Recession rates of up to 0.48 metres per year have been measured on the Chalk at Culver Cliff[57]. Apart from the landslides at Bonchurch, Blackgang, and along sectors of the north coast, it has been estimated that the cliffs at Rocken End have been receding at 0.6 metres/year, and that those bordering Brighstone Bay have been cut back 0.3 to 0.5 metres/year[58]. Average rates in metres per year can vary with the period considered, and can be much influenced by a single major change. For example, Dr. W.H. Fitton observed that a crack appeared in the cliffs near Atherfield Point in 1844, parallel to the cliff crest and about 24 metres back from it. A slice of the cliff 45 metres long then subsided to the shore, disintegrated and was soon washed away by the waves[14].

Local changes have included the collapse of one of the original stacks at the Needles, Lot's Wife, in a storm in 1764, and the foundering of an arch that connected the innermost of the Needles to the mainland in 1810. Arch Rock in Freshwater Bay (Fig. 23) collapsed in a storm in October 1992.

Man-made Landforms

Earthworks of various kinds have modified the land surface locally. Some of these date from prehistoric times, such as the Bronze Age barrows (tumuli) on Afton Down (352857), Shalcombe Down (391855) and Gallows Hill near Downend (536874). Early fortifications include Castle Hill, above Mottistone (409841), Centurion's Hill (622869) east of Brading, and the defensive embankment on the southern slopes of Bembridge Down (627855).

There are also small man-made depressions in the Chalk country where pits have been cut to extract gravel, flints, marl or stone. There is a good example of such a pit, probably used to extract marl from the Lower Chalk, on the southern slopes of Bembridge Down (627854). More recent man-made landforms include road and railway cuttings and embankments, quarries, reclamation features (such as the meadows of the Eastern Yar below Brading), quays (as alongside the Medina estuary at Cowes) and various kinds of sea walls and promenades along the coast.

Conclusion

Various processes have combined to shape the landforms that have developed on the various geological formations and structures seen on the Isle of Wight. The next Chapter presents an excursion around the island coastline, on which the relationships between geology and coastal scenery are well displayed.

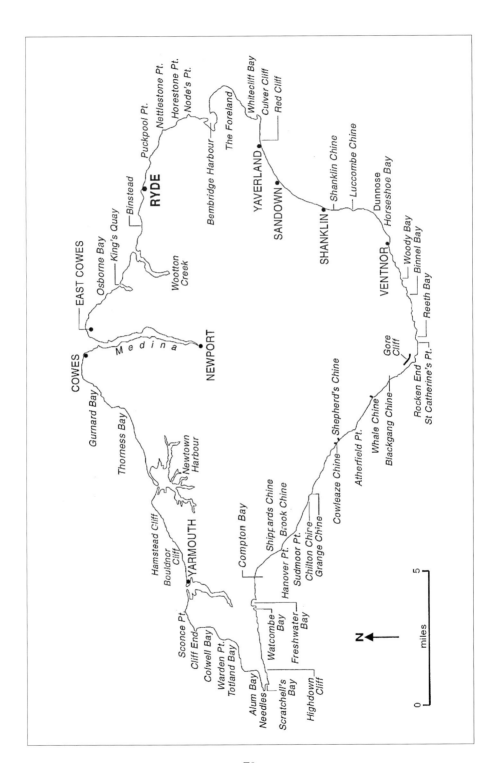

70

AROUND THE COAST OF
THE ISLE OF WIGHT

Introduction

The coastline of the Isle of Wight is about 56 miles (90 km) long (Fig. 24). The best way of seeing it is to walk round the island, using the Coastal Footpath and, where possible, going along the shore at low tide. Much more can be seen when the tide is out, and foreshore features are exposed and accessible. It is necessary to study local tide tables (obtainable in Information Centres) or check tidal predictions (published in the Isle of Wight County Press, each Friday, with high tide predictions for the ensuing week) in order to decide the best time to explore the coast. Days when the tide is falling during the morning are ideal, because the foreshore is then accessible for several hours, but it is usually possible to plan an excursion that goes along the shore when the tide is low, and to follow the Coastal Footpath back when it is high. Local bus services are useful, especially in summer, and those who travel by car will need to use the car parks (labelled P on the Isle of Wight Outdoor Leisure map) and to walk intervening coastal sectors.

This account of a clockwise circuit of the island coast is broken into sections that begin and end at points accessible from car parks, or close to bus stops. Some will be able to persuade car-borne friends to meet them at the end of each coastal sector, preferably with the makings of a good picnic.

Hazards

It is necessary to draw attention to the various hazards that may be encountered in exploring the coastal geology and scenery of the Isle of Wight (see Notice on page 11). Exposures of geological formations are mainly found on steep coastal cliffs, which are dangerous, not only because of the risk of falling over them (especially on windy days), but because of frequent slumping. People have been killed or injured by falling rocks and slumping debris, and when examining geological sections a hard hat should be worn. Hammering and quarrying cliffs for fossils or minerals is a hazardous pastime. After rainy periods it is difficult to climb over fallen rocks, which are often unstable, and landslides can become

Opposite, Fig. 24: Coastal excursion.

very soft and sticky, and almost impossible to traverse. It is unwise to visit the cliffy shores of the Isle of Wight alone in winter or in windy or wet weather.

In walking along the shore to examine a geological outcrop or landform feature there is a risk of being cut off by the rising tide or washed over by large waves. Accidents have occurred when people have tried to climb cliffs to escape these hazards.

TRAVERSES

Ryde to St. Helen's Church

The pier at Ryde provides a good view over the extensive sandy area exposed at low tide in front of the Ryde promenade and out across Spithead to Portsmouth. The intertidal zone is here unusually wide, probably because it is underlain by ledges of sandstone or limestone. Ryde is built on a north-facing slope in which the Bembridge Marls overlie the Osborne Marls (Lower Oligocene), but these are not well exposed on the shore.

The walk begins east of the pier, where the coastal fringe contains the railway, a marina, a hovercraft terminal, and funfairs. The Esplanade runs behind a sandy beach and across the mouth of the valley of Monktonmead Brook, where a former embayment has been enclosed as a small lake. At Appley it continues in front of rising ground on the Osborne Beds, a parkland with hummocky slopes indicating past instability. The Coastal Path is then followed along the top of an artificial embankment, backed by a small hollow and a wooded slope, at the base of which there are outcrops of clay and some minor rubbly limestone layers in the Osborne Marls. The coast curves out to Puckpool Point, the sandy beach becoming gravelly, with brown sandstone cobbles and small boulders on the shore. Out to sea are No Man's Land fort, and beyond it Horse Sand fort, structures built between 1869 and 1880 when a French invasion was feared.

As these forts come into line, the sea wall curves round towards Spring Vale, and there is a view along the shore to Nettlestone Point. Puckpool Hill road comes down to the coast at the Battery Inn, and Springvale Road then runs behind a modern sea wall that has gates to be closed against exceptionally high tides and storm surges. Streams draining two small valleys are piped under the road and the sea wall to discharge on to the shore. This was probably the site of Barnsley Harbour, which existed hereabouts in the 17th century[59]. A shingle beach with many intact sea shells is fronted by sand, strewn with pieces of brown and grey calcareous sandstone. Towards Seaview these become ledges outcropping on the shore and rising towards Nettlestone Point, where the sandy intertidal zone narrows and almost fades out.

These ledges are the outcrop of the resistant Nettlestone Grits, shelly calcareous sands and sandstones about 6 metres thick, overlain and underlain by marls. On the western side of Nettlestone Point some blocks of calcareous sandstone have been assembled as groynes. Rocky ledges continue past the Seaview Yacht Club slipway, and become higher and bolder on the eastern side of Nettlestone Point, diverging south-eastward from the shore as declining reefs (Fig. 25).

Fig. 25: Dissected shore ledges of Nettlestone Grit on the eastern side of Nettlestone Point.

From Nettlestone Point the Coastal Footpath runs inland behind Seagrove Bay, but at low tide it is possible to walk along the sandy beach to Horestone Point, and on along Priory Bay past Nodes Point to the ruins of St. Helens Church. In Seagrove Bay the beach is backed by wooded bluffs on the marls that overlie the Nettlestone Grits, and a concrete wall extends round a reclaimed salient in front of the Old Boathouse. There is an upper beach of shingle behind the sandy shore. The bluffs curve out to Horestone Point, on the northern side of which is a small but deep-seated rotational landslide where the Bembridge Limestone and Bembridge Marls have subsided over soft Osborne Marls (p. 63). Wooden stakes were inserted to protect the cliff base, but these have become tilted as the result of continuing instability[50].

A fault running across the shore brings up the Nettlestone Grits, which form large blocks and boulders, again partly arranged into artificial groynes. This outcrop of hard calcareous sandstone with flint pebbles and shells is responsible for the Horestone Point promontory, which declines into a bouldery shore draped with sea wrack. A way can be found through the boulders, which are reddish-brown and ferruginous[13]. On the promontory the Nettlestone Grits are overlain by the St. Helens Beds, consisting of soft fine white sand passing up into green and yellow clay and sand, capped by the marl which forms the coastal slope. The hinterland consists of a wide plateau, rising gently from 40 to 50 metres southward through Nettlestone towards St. Helens, strewn with Pleistocene Marine Gravel, and incised by valleys that run down to bays on the coast. On the southern side of Nettlestone Point the upper part of the Nettlestone Grits can be traced laterally into a hard marl and then a shelly limestone (page 38).

South of Horestone Point the walk continues along the wide sands of Priory Bay, in front of wooded bluffs in which the St. Helens Beds decline beneath Bembridge Marls. The base of the bluffs is at first protected from wave attack by a shingle beach, and there is a broad shallow lagoon offshore, bordered seaward by a sandy shoal extending north towards Horestone Point, which also diminishes wave action. The shingle beach fades out in front of segments of a masonry wall which formerly protected the bluffs southward to Nodes Point, but has fallen into disrepair. Behind gaps in the wall the base of the bluffs has been cliffed by wave attack, exposing stratified rock and clay, the Bembridge Limestone beneath the Bembridge Marls. The sandy beach comes to an end, and blocks of wrack-covered limestone run out across the shore.

Nodes Point protrudes as the Bembridge Limestone rises to form shore ledges and a bouldery reef. There is a cliff cut in layers of limestone and clay at the base of the wooded bluffs, and it is possible to walk round the point at low tide and on southward along a sandy beach in front of slumping bluffs of grey and brown Bembridge Marls, from the base of which layers of Bembridge Limestone emerge, and eventually run out as ledges across the shore (Fig. 26). The Bembridge Limestone here consists of about 6 metres of massive freshwater limestone with intercalated greenish clays. The top is uneven and capped by a black oyster bed, then the brown clay of the Bembridge Marls. Clays lubricated by seeping groundwater are sliding over the sea wall. The ledges are developed on an upper shelly and partly ferruginous limestone, separated by washed-out layers of laminated green clay from an earthy lower limestone. The southward-dipping limestone has been dissected along joints and bedding-planes, dividing the ledges into a series of rocky spurs, between which are little beaches of sand

Above, Fig. 26: Shore ledges of Bembridge Limestone dipping southward from Nodes Point.

Below: Fig. 27: Ledges of Bembridge Limestone looking across the mouth of Bembridge Harbour (Bouldnor Syncline) towards Bembridge.

and flint pebbles. At low tide a wide area strewn with limestone boulders and flint gravel is exposed, out towards St. Helens Fort, another of the nineteenth century Spithead forts.

The ledges of Bembridge Limestone dip below low tide off the ruins of St Helens Church, across the axis of the Bouldnor Syncline, and rise again in Tyne Ledge, off Bembridge Point, south of the Yar estuary (Fig. 27). This estuary has been formed by submergence of a river valley cut out along the eastern part of the Bouldnor syncline. There is a car park south of St Helens Church, and buses returning to Ryde leave from St. Helens, at the top of the hill.

St. Helens Church to Bembridge

Behind St. Helens Church the coastal bluffs pass inland as a gentler wooded slope, but the sand and gravel beach continues southward, forming the seaward shore of a broad spit, The Duver, which constricts the mouth of the River Yar estuary, also known as Bembridge Harbour. Footpaths lead inland over low dunes, with short grassland intensively grazed by rabbits on the landward side and taller marram grass on the seaward side. This was the site of the Royal Isle of Wight golf course, and is now a National Trust property. Its seaward margin has been cut back, and is protected by a sea wall, with groynes designed to retain the sand and shingle beach. At low tide the outflow channel from Bembridge Harbour (marked by red and green buoys) swings first northward between the lobe of shingle at the end of The Duver and a smaller outer intertidal spit protruding from Bembridge Point, then curves eastward to the sea south of St. Helens Island.

Inland, across The Duver, the Coastal Footpath runs along a stone wall, the Old Mill Dam, with bridged gaps, on the northern shore of Bembridge Harbour. This wall borders a tidal lagoon with salt marshes (including much Spartina grass) to the east (Fig. 28) and green weedy mudflats to the west. There was formerly a tide mill here. The Coastal Footpath continues to Latimer Road, then runs south-east along the B3395 on an embankment bordering Bembridge Harbour. This causeway was built in 1878 on the southern side of the harbour, and B3395 follows it round to Bembridge Point, opposite the Pilot Boat Inn. Bembridge Harbour, a wide pool at high tide, has a low tide channel between mud and sand shoals, with patches of eelgrass (Zostera), and is a harbour for yachts and motor boats.

Bembridge Harbour is the remains of the much larger Brading Harbour[60]. Late in the nineteenth century there was extensive land reclamation here, the River Yar being confined to an embanked channel downstream from Brading,

Above, Fig. 28: Salt marsh terrace bordering a tidal creek behind the Duver spit, St. Helens.

Below, Fig. 29: Bembridge Pier, showing shore ledges of Bembridge Limestone.

between broad rushy meadows on the site of former mudflats and salt marshes. These can be seen by making a detour along a footpath from Carpenters, west of St. Helens, following the line of the old railway to Brading railway station, and returning by way of Bembridge Trail, crossing the river at the bridge (616871). This Trail climbs Centurion's Hill, past prehistoric earthworks, and runs behind the low wooded bluffs cut in Bembridge Marls on the southern edge of the flood-plain, beside the airport and so up to the windmill and into Bembridge from the south-west.

Bembridge Point is a broad, blunt dune-capped spit with a shingle beach fronted by sand on its seaward side. To the east the ground rises behind a scrubby slope that steepens to a bluff with breakaways above landslides in gravel-capped Bembridge Marls and some clay lobes truncated by wave erosion behind the beach. The Coastal Footpath runs along Pump Lane (opposite the Row Barge Inn) and Ducie Avenue to come out on the wooded bluff behind Colonel's Hard, where there are broad shore ledges on the brown Bembridge Limestone as it rises from the Bouldnor Syncline. The shingle beach extends along the shore in front of the bluff past East Cliff and Tyne Hall, and is divided by many groynes and eventually backed by a sea wall. The footpath follows the shore, as sandflats exposed at low tide narrow south-eastward, and at their outer edge a reef of Bembridge Limestone, Tyne Ledge, runs in to the beach beneath the pier that bears the Bembridge Lifeboat Station. To seaward are two more reefs, one of which passes beneath the outer end of this pier (Fig. 29).

The pier can be reached by car from Bembridge Point by driving up Sherbourne Street, past the Maritime Museum, right into High Street, left into Foreland Road to a T-junction; and left again into Lane End Road. There is a small car park in Fishermans Walk, near the head of the pier, and buses from Bembridge, half a mile inland, run back to St. Helens.

Bembridge and the Foreland

Bembridge can be reached by bus from Ryde, and some will want to walk the next few sectors, along the coast southward to Whitecliff Point then over the Chalk ridge at Bembridge Down, descending to the coast at Yaverland.

From Bembridge Pier the Coastal Footpath runs along the top of the low cliffs, but soon turns inland through Foreland Farm Lane. In order to see the Foreland it is best to walk on along the shingle beach in front of low slumping cliffs cut in dark Bembridge Marls capped by gravels in a clay matrix. The foreshore consists of ledges of Bembridge Limestone with seaward-facing scarplets, separated by sandy corridors where intervening marls have been etched out along the geological strike. These ledges run on south-eastward, diverging from the coast as the low cliffs, fronted by a sea wall, curve round the Foreland, facing eastward then south-eastward.

Behind these low cliffs Bembridge is built on a plateau where the Bembridge Marls are overlain by Marine Gravel, mainly flint and chert, with some pebbles from the Eocene and a few from the Greensand outcrops to the south. Marine Gravel exposed in the cliffs south of the Foreland (Fig. 30) is a Pleistocene Raised Beach, resting on a bench cut into the Bembridge Marls, and banked against a backing cliff[61]. It has a capping of loamy Brickearth, deposited by wind action (p. 45).

Fig. 30: Cliff cut in Bembridge Raised Beach gravels south of The Foreland.

Off the Foreland the Bembridge Ledges are parallel outcrops of Bembridge Limestone that change direction from NW-SE to NE-SW as they cross a minor syncline running eastward. They are structural shore platforms in the sense that each of the gently-inclined ledges corresponds with the upper surface of a limestone layer, the overlying softer clay having been washed away. This part of the coast is sheltered from the strong wave action generated by the prevailing westerly and south-westerly winds in the English Channel, and wave energy has been too weak for the cutting of an abrasion ramp across the outcropping strata.

Whitecliff Bay

The footpath follows the sea wall round the Foreland, and there is a view south-westward past the Chalk promontory at Whitecliff Point to the high promontory at Dunnose. The sea wall comes to an end with a sandy beach in front of a scrubby undercliff terrace where there are several wooden shacks. This undercliff is backed by a cliff cut into the Raised Beach gravels. The Coastal Footpath (656874) comes in from Foreland Farm Lane and the Crab and Lobster Inn, and continues along the top of the cliffs behind Whitecliff Bay, but the best way to see the coastal landforms is to walk on southward along the beach at low tide.

Ledges of brown Bembridge Limestone continue along the shore, the inner and outer reefs separated by a corridor of gravelly sand which declines into a low tide channel known as The Run. The ledges are strewn with seaweed and partly concealed by sand. They curve round the Foreland, dipping landward to form a shallow trough. Another low tide channel is between the inner reef, Black Rock Ledge, and the outer reef, Long Ledge, which runs in towards the coast to pass beneath the Bembridge Marls in the cliffs of Howgate Bay (645873). At the cliff base there are outcrops of a thin, dark Oyster Bed just above the junction between the Bembridge Limestone and the overlying Bembridge Marls. Slabs of grey siltstone on the beach have come from an outcrop a little higher in the broken slopes of Bembridge Marls.

The cliff crest gradually rises south-westward towards Bembridge School, receding behind landslide topography where the gravelly deposits have slumped down over the soft Bembridge Marls. Slumping is active here, particularly after wet weather when water percolating through the gravels lubricates the underlying marls. To the south the lower cliff steepens as the topmost layers of the Bembridge Limestone appear at the cliff base, and the coast curves out to a small promontory, Black Rock Point. As it does so, a cliff-base ledge of knobbly grey limestone becomes prominent, rising gradually along the eastern shore of this promontory. Another ledge comes in at a lower level, the thin intervening clay having been washed out. At a higher level there is irregular topography on Bembridge Marls, which here consist of green, blue, grey and red clays and marls with some sands and thin limestones. The landslide topography narrows as the Bembridge Limestone rises, the cliff profile steepening. Southward the limestone ledges become dissected, with intervening small coves containing beaches of brown and blue flint cobbles and pebbles with some sand. The limestones here show fluting and other corrosion features, as well as local abrasion by waves armed with sand and pebbles (Fig. 31).

The basal limestone ledge, carpeted with green weed, comes in to the cliff base and rises southward. Tabular blocks of fallen limestone litter the shore.

Above, Fig. 31: Weathering features on Bembridge Limestone at Black Rock. The limestone has been pitted by solution processes and abraded by the movement of beach gravels. Below, Fig. 32: Ledges of Bembridge Limestone at Black Rock, with a limestone layer rising southward into Whitecliff Bay.

The cliff steepens further as four main bands of limestone, with intervening dark clays, rise to dominate it. A conspicuous white limestone layer runs along the cliff, rising gently at first, then more steeply as the northward dip suddenly increases, curving up to the cliff crest, underlain by clays and marls (Fig. 32).

Along the shore to the south is a gently curving cliffed coast cut across the steeply-dipping soft Lower Oligocene, Eocene and Palaeocene formations. The geological sequences seen here and in Alum Bay (p. 130) are of international importance, representing cycles of sedimentation that occurred between 30 and 60 million years ago, from the late Palaeocene to the early Oligocene, yielding about 600 metres of strata in a kilometre of coast. Below the upward-curving Bembridge Limestone the cliffs are cut into a succession of thin clays, siltstones and sandstones, dipping northward at 70° to 80°, and much disturbed by slumping. These are shown on the geological map as Osborne and Headon Beds, but are now known as the Headon Hill Formation, with subdivisions described in the Geologists' Association Guide[2]. They extend south to a pathway ascending from the beach, beyond which the clayey beds give place to the yellow Barton Sand, which dominates the steep triangular cliff to the south. Next comes a hollow excavated in the soft grey sandy clays and silts of the Barton Clay, through which a ramp leads up to the Whitecliff Bay caravan park.

Road access to Whitecliff Bay from Bembridge is along the B3385 (Sandown Road) to Steyne Cross, then Hillway Road to Peacock Hill Farm, from which a footpath leads down through the Whitecliff Bay caravan park to the coast. Parking is often possible at the nearby Activity Centre, from which footpaths run through to the coast.

The small steep-sided incised valley with a curving ramp below the Whitecliff Bay caravan park is an example of a chine (p. 55). The cliffs of Whitecliff Bay are receding, erosion having accelerated after 1904, when the shingle beach that formerly protected them was depleted by the removal of gravel for use in the building of Bembridge Fort on the crest of the Chalk ridge to the south[62]. The beach is now mostly sandy, backed by a narrow strip of shingle.

South of the curving ramp (behind the café) the northward dip of rock formations in the cliffs steepens until the strata stand almost vertical. A prominent dark flint gravel layer marks the base of the Bracklesham Beds, 180 metres thick, which consist of alternations of coherent sands forming high cliffs and softer clays and shales cut out as hollows and gullies. Then come the Bagshot Sands, about 40 metres of cross-bedded yellow, grey and white sands with thin grey pipe-clay bands (Fig. 33). The cliff is trenched by a series of ravines cut in the softer strata, alternating with ribs and ridges on the harder sandstones. The Bagshot Beds are followed by 90 metres of brown clays and silts, the London Clay, with wide chines containing small landslides on either side of a sandy

Above, Fig. 33: Cliff cut in Bagshot Sands, Whitecliff Bay, the gulley on the right being cut in clays at the bottom of the Bracklesham Beds.
Below, Fig. 34: Cliffs cut in London Clay, Whitecliff Bay, showing slumping hollows in clay on either side of a spur of vertical sandstone (left).

spur (Fig. 34), and then a narrow cliffed ridge on the pebbly sands of the thin (3 metre) Oldhaven Formation, with flints derived from the Chalk. The sequence is completed across a broad (50 metre) slumping valley cut into the Palaeocene Reading Beds, which here consist of subsiding soft pink, red and mottled grey clays, with a basal wave-cut ramp at the back of the shore.

The Reading Beds are banked against a steep wall of Chalk which forms the southern shore of Whitecliff Bay (Fig. 35). At their base is about a metre of flinty and loamy sand with broken, unworn flints and some flint pebbles, resting on, and patchily adhering to, the steeply inclined surface of rubbly Chalk, which is irregular with potholes up to a foot in diameter containing loose flints and chalky sand. The gravelly sand at the base of the Reading Beds is probably the remains of a subaerial drift deposit that had formed on the horizontal or gently sloping plain cut into the Chalk. It was submerged and reworked by the waves of the rising Palaeocene sea. Some pebbles and cobbles of Chalk and white-coated fresh flint nodules are present in the existing gravelly beach, which runs northward from here, fading out in front of the London Clay outcrop.

Fig. 35: The promontory at Whitecliff Point, showing grassy slopes on slumped chalk rubble and a basal platform extending eastward (left).

Whitecliff Point

On the southern side of Whitecliff Bay the cliff is cut into the Upper Chalk, dipping northward at about 65° and forming a high partly vegetated bluff with talus slopes, extending eastward for about 200 metres. Seen from the north (Fig. 35), the profile is very steep, with a large notch at the base, from which a shore platform, submerged at high tide, extends out in front of a high cliff that faces south-eastward. A path leads along the base of the cliff, which shows a stepped series of steeply-dipping bedding-planes, and as the cliff is set back a shore platform, cut across the steeply dipping chalk layers, develops and widens eastward to about 25 metres at Whitecliff Point (Fig. 22).

The shore platform is strewn with large and small chalk boulders, and shows steeply-inclined ribs that extend eastward between wave-scoured furrows, some with elongated pools at low tide. There are protruding layers and nodules of flint. The platform declines gradually below the low tide line, and has been shaped mainly by wave action, assisted by the presence of hard flints that scour the rock surface as they are moved to and fro by the waves. It is interesting to speculate on why there is a well-developed shore platform here at the eastern end of the central Chalk ridge of the Isle of Wight, and not in the similar geological situation on Ballard Point, where steeply-dipping Chalk is truncated at the eastern end of the Purbeck (Hills) ridge in Dorset[9].

On walking round Whitecliff Point, the high cliff is seen to rise behind the shore platform, with a notch or concave swash slope at its base (Fig. 36). The freshly abraded chalk is white, in contrast with the green grey algal surfaces on the shore platform and in the weathered cliff. Parallel flint layers mark out the bedding, sweeping upward through the cliff face to jagged crests. The Upper Chalk is here about 310 metres thick.

At Whitecliff Point the Upper Chalk is massive and hard, with irregular flint layers including some large tabular nodules along the bedding planes, and seams of marl. The cliff facing south-east is cut in steeply-dipping chalk strata with numerous seams of marl, curving to a protruding nose of hard massive flintless Chalk, with higher ribs running out across the shore. There is a little cove of blue-grey flint shingle to the south, backed by a vertical to overhanging cliff of compact white chalk with few marl seams and rather sparse layers of small flints. Minor caves are angled to the bedding planes. The jutting spur called the Anvil is formed of massive white chalk with few marl seams and sparse layers of small flints, its grassy northern slope following a bedding-plane which has been exposed by erosion along a weaker overlying horizon (Fig. 37).

It is possible at low tide to scramble round the end of the Anvil, along a chalk ledge, and to look down into Horseshoe Cove, a bouldery inlet with twin caves,

Above, Fig. 36: Basal notch at Whitecliff Point, undercut by waves armed with flint gravel.

Below, Fig. 37: The Anvil, a promontory extending out from the southern side of Whitecliff Point. The grassy slope follows the dip of a bedding-plane.

known as The Nostrils, in the base of the cliff (Fig. 38). Beyond these another rib of hard rock runs out from the cliff, and ends with an outlying angular low stack, Shag Rock. The dip diminishes to 48° in the pale grey hard nodular chalk at this southern point.

The shore then becomes inaccessible, even at low tide (except by boat), as the coast swings westward into Culver Cliff, and it is necessary to return to the caravan site in Whitecliff Bay and take the Coastal Footpath up to Bembridge Down. Those using a car can drive back to the B3395, past Bembridge Airport, and skirt the Chalk ridge until a sharp left turning leads up to the crest of Bembridge Down.

Fig. 38: The Nostrils, twin caves excavated in Upper Chalk on the southern side of Whitecliff Point.

Bembridge Down

From Whitecliff Bay the Coastal Footpath runs southward along the gently rising top of the cliffs, past the heads of chines cut into the Eocene and Palaeocene outcrops. Above the caravan park it curves round the head of a large dell cut into London Clay, then goes along the edge of a field and into a wood, where steps climb the steepening slope of the Chalk. These lead up to a stile, beyond which a chalk path runs diagonally up the grassy slope ridge, then along between blackthorn hedges before ascending to the Earl of Yarborough Monument on Culver Down. The crest of the ridge rises to about 100 metres above sea level, and there are fine views in all directions.

Northward, across Bembridge Airport, is the broad valley floor of the Eastern Yar, opening to the estuary of Bembridge Harbour, the ground beyond rising gently to Seaview and Ryde.

To the north-east, back across Whitecliff Bay, is the Bembridge Plateau, with the windmill on its southern edge, and to the right are the cliffs extending to the Foreland, with Bembridge Ledges exposed offshore at low tide. Beyond, across Spithead, are Portsmouth and Southsea, backed by the Chalk ridge of Ports Down, and away to the east the coast curves out to low-lying Selsey Bill, the dip-slope of the South Downs rising behind the low Sussex coastal plain: on a clear day the spire of Chichester cathedral may be seen.

To the west the high central Chalk ridge extends along Bembridge Down, is breached by the River Yar gap at Brading, then continues westward on Brading Down, Ashey Down with its prominent sea mark, and Mersley Down, towards Newport. On its southern side is the broad undulating lowland on Lower Greensand formations, extending past Godshill and rising to a wide gap between the south-facing Chalk and Upper Greensand escarpments of Chillerton Down and Berry Hill and the equivalent north-facing escarpments on St. Catherine's Down. This is where the Sandown Anticline has been excavated into Lower Greensand and the Wealden Beds, the covering arch of Chalk and Upper Greensand having been breached and removed; in other words, a denuded anticline, a small version of the 'inverted relief' seen in the Weald, between the North Downs and the South Downs in south-east England[63].

There is also a fine view south-westward across Sandown Bay to the sandstone cliffs towards Shanklin and Luccombe, the high promontory of Dunnose, and the southern Chalk plateau rising to about 240 metres on Wroxall Down.

Bembridge Down to Yaverland

From the Monument on Culver Down the Coastal Path descends the Chalk escarpment of Bembridge Down to follow the cliff edge, which is dissected by rabbit burrows. The cliff crest begins to decline westward as the upper convexity grows into the steep grassy escarpment that forms the southern slopes of Bembridge Down. Culver Cliff is cut into the lower part of this escarpment, exposing Upper, Middle and Lower Chalk and the Upper Greensand. A prominent embankment (627854) is an earthwork, for at the top of the cliff the preceding soil horizon can be seen to run beneath it, and there is a hollow downslope now largely occupied by earthy gravel. The cliff crest then falls and rises through a hollow (a col) across the head of a dry valley that descends westward to Yaverland. This valley was cut by stream action when the water table stood higher, or when runoff was augmented by melting snow over frost-shattered rock and frozen ground during cold phases of the Late Pleistocene. The bottom of the valley runs along the Gault outcrop, the bordering slopes being cut into the overlying Upper Greensand and Lower Chalk marls to the north and into the underlying Lower Greensand (Carstone, Sandrock and Ferruginous Sands), rising to Red Cliff on the southern side. The cliff edge is fenced out, but from the col it is possible to see the soft dark Gault Clay outcrop, and to look eastward over the Upper Greensand to the Chalk of Culver Cliff.

The cliff crest then rises to the top of Red Cliff, an almost vertical cliff cut in the Ferruginous Sands formation. Towards the western end the grey shales of the Atherfield Clay rise into the base of the cliff, and as they do so the cliff crest recedes behind a wide landslide, backed by cracking and disintegrating sandy breakaways and subsiding slices and tilted ridges of sandstone over Atherfield Clay and the clays and shales of the Wealden Beds. The landslide becomes narrower as the upper cliff descends westward through these softer formations. In dry weather it is possible to scramble down a track to the beach from the Sandown Bay caravan and chalet centre, but otherwise the Coastal Footpath can be followed on down to the Yaverland car park, where there is easy access to the beach. There is usually a good view onward to the sandstone cliffs between Sandown and Shanklin, where the strata decline, then rise again as they cross the shallow Lake Syncline (p. 94).

The road from Bembridge Down runs back down to the B3395, which swings southward through Yaverland to the coastal car park.

Below Culver Cliff

It is best to hike eastward along the shore from Yaverland car park to Culver Cliff, and then to examine the underlying formations in more detail on the way back. In this way it is possible to maintain the downward sequence through the Cretaceous formations below the Upper Chalk of Whitecliff Point. The cliffs are cut across the successive formations dipping northward off the Sandown Anticline, from the Chalk and Upper Greensand down through the Gault and Lower Greensand to the Vectis and Wessex Formations of the Wealden Beds, which outcrop around the anticlinal axis at Sandown.

Culver Cliff has been cut into the south-facing Chalk escarpment by marine erosion. There is an upper grassy convex slope above the very steep white cliff, which has grassy patches. The stratified Chalk dips about 55° northward into the cliff, the Upper Chalk rising to the top near the eastern end, with the Middle and Lower Chalk below. There are minor benches on the outcrops of thin but hard nodular bands, the Chalk Rock near the top of the Middle Chalk and the Melbourn Rock at the bottom of that formation. The cliff gradient diminishes gradually below the Melbourn Rock, and the cliff is set back along the underlying Plenus marls, a conspicuous band of blue-grey marls and pale grey limestones. Below this is a gentler slope in about 75 metres of the soft, marly Lower Chalk[64], at the base of which is a layer of calcareous doggers (rounded blocks of sandstone).

The shore below Culver Cliff is lined by large fallen boulders of Chalk and Upper Greensand. Flints from the Upper Chalk have weathered out to form irregular stony nodules, initially white-rinded or bluish cobbles, which have accumulated as a cobble beach. At low tide a set of parallel shore ridges cut into the steeply-dipping layers of Chalk and Upper Greensand can be seen diverging east-south-eastward from the shore.

The Middle and Lower Chalk are stratified in Culver Cliff, but become frost-shattered as they pass westward into the escarpment, where they are mantled by an earthy gravel. There have been many rock falls from this shattered Chalk.

The Lower Chalk is underlain by 30 metres of pale yellow, light green and blue grey bedded sandstones of the Upper Greensand, somewhat obscured by slumping, then the cliff crest descends past the earthwork (mentioned above) into a hollow on the narrow outcrop of the blue-black Gault clay, which has slumped and been washed down the steep slope. There is earthy gravel at the top of the cliff, with angular flints that have moved down from the Chalk escarpment during Pleistocene episodes of periglacial sludging. The cliff rises again on the Carstone, a red-brown ferruginous sandstone with some quartzite pebbles, and the underlying Sandrock Beds, consisting of paler (yellow, brown

Above, Fig, 39: Red Cliff, showing the slumping Gault on the right, and the steeply-dipping dark Carstone, paler Sandrock and Ferruginous Sands on the left, fronted by a cobble beach.

Below: Fig. 40: Red Cliff, showing the Ferruginous Sands underlain by the Atherfield Clay, over which sandy material has slumped in the foreground. Culver Cliff in the distance.

and white) sands (Fig. 39). Red Cliff stands almost vertical in the thicker and more resistant Ferruginous Sands, brown and red-brown sandstones (the iron compounds have been reddened by oxidation) with pebble beds at various levels, ascending south-westward along the coast (Fig. 40).

Returning along the shore, the grey and brown silty Atherfield Clay is seen at the base of the cliff, rising south-westward. As has been noted, the cliff crest recedes behind landslides developed on the Atherfield Clay, which rises westward through the slumped topography, the cliff crest in Ferruginous Sands receding behind a broad amphitheatre of slumped sand and clay (Fig. 41). Clay lobes have been truncated along the shore by low cliffs cut by marine erosion, and occasional layers of grey and yellow sandstone form bolder outcrops within the sloping cliffs. There is a gravelly upper beach, fronted by a sandy shore exposed at low tide.

Fig. 41: The Yaverland landslide, with scrubby vegetation on subsided material over the Atherfield Clay, looking towards Sandown.

Segments of a blue-green glauconitic fossiliferous muddy sandstone appear (about 350 metres east of the car park) as a shore reef that runs in to the beach of sand backed by shingle. This is the Perna Bed, up to 2 metres thick at the base of the Atherfield Clay. Its outcrop runs up across the beach and ascends through the low sloping clay cliffs towards Yaverland as a bolder vertical feature. The cliffs are slumping, cut into the underlying grey Vectis Shales (formerly Wealden Shales), and within these are two thin limestones, then a ledge of yellow sandstone rising westward[65]. There is a shingle beach, below which is a wave-cut ramp in mottled clay, exposed as the tide ebbs. At the base of the Vectis Shales a pale grey fine sandstone bed also ascends westward through the cliff. Then pink, mottled grey, blue and purple marls appear in the crumbling cliffs of the Wessex Marls (formerly Wealden Marls), capped by an earthy soil with angular flints (Fig. 42). The cliffs disappear behind the concrete sea wall at the Yaverland Car Park and the first of the many wooden groynes that divide the sandy beach of Sandown, built to prevent the sand drifting away eastward along the shore.

Those who have walked from Bembridge may wish to return there by bus from this point.

Fig. 42: The cliffs cut in the Wessex Marls Formation (Wealden) east of Yaverland, looking towards the Chalk of Culver Cliff.

Sandown Bay

Sandown Bay has been excavated in the Wealden Beds (Vectis Shales underlain by Wessex Marls) which occupy the core of the unroofed Sandown Anticline. These forms an undulating lowland, fringed by a narrow outcrop of Atherfield Clay, which is concealed beneath the Sandown esplanade and seafront structures, although it is possible to find scattered pebbles of material from the Perna Bed on the beach. The axis of the Sandown Anticline is marked by tabular reefs exposed on the shore at low tide near the Sandown Zoo, which are outcrops of a brown calcareous sandstone in the Wessex Marls. On the southern side of the anticline outcrops of the Vectis and Wessex Formations are hidden by the sea wall and buildings. The beach of yellow and brown sand (derived mainly from the Lower Greensand) consists of a convex upper beach descending to a low tide gravelly zone, which at times is covered by fine dark grey wet sand that moves in from the sea floor in calm weather, but is withdrawn during stormy periods. Southward the coast curves gently until it faces almost due east.

The town of Sandown is built on a plateau on the overlying Ferruginous Sands, which form the higher country on the southern side of the anticline. The coast between Sandown and Shanklin consists of almost vertical cliffs 20 to 30 metres high in this formation, with basal talus covered by grasses and scrub, fronted by a sea wall and undercliff walk (Fig. 43). The cliff-top footpath runs behind a fence, and does not give good views of the cliffs.

South of the pier the cliff section behind the Undercliff Walk runs in front of cliffs that show about 10 metres of light yellow or brown weathered sands over 15 metres of buff to grey-green loamy sandstone, with a seepage zone at the contact. The strata (which are equivalent to the sandstones seen in the cliffs below Blackgang, p. 111) dip southward along the coast at about 5° on the southern side of the Sandown Anticline, the lower division disappearing from view south of Lake Slipway. The upper division changes from light brown to dark green as it passes below the weathered zone, and this, too disappears from view north of Little Stairs. It is overlain by 10 metres of coarse compact greensand which is again light brown at first, in the weathered zone, and grey-green as it declines below the seepage zone. South of Lake Slipway 8 metres of dark loamy greensand appears at the cliff top and descends to the middle of the cliff section at Little Stairs. This in turn is capped by up to 14 metres of brown loamy sands. The cliffs show little variation across these divisions, but cliff face weathering includes flaking and the formation of breached "windows". South of Little Stairs is a sector of slumped and vegetated slope in a zone where faulting has brought the brown loamy sands down on the southern side; the strata are then almost horizontal across the shallow Lake Syncline, before rising slightly towards

Shanklin. Along the cliff crest is a capping of up to 1.5 metres of earthy gravel.

In front of the sea wall, built in 1971, the beach at high tide is narrow, and in places absent, but at low tide a wide sandy shore is exposed. Small Hope Beach is retained by a groyne, and a broader protrusion to the south has intercepted drifting sand to form Hope Beach, which narrows southward to Appley Beach. The cliff disappears behind an artificial slope where the road descends to Shanklin esplanade, and when it reappears it is at first draped with vegetation and partly hidden by trees. It continues behind the Chair Lift and the hotels and shops of Shanklin, where the Ferruginous Sands show a gentle northward dip on the southern side of the Lake Syncline, rising over the gentle Shanklin Anticline.

Above, Fig. 43: Cliffs cut in Ferruginous Sands at Lake Slipway, between Sandown and Shanklin.

Shanklin to Dunnose

Shanklin esplanade comes to an end in a slipway, the narrow sandy beach continuing as Appley Beach, backed by an upper beach of coarse flint and greensand gravel. A detour may be made up Shanklin Chine, a deep wooded valley with a stream incised into reddish brown sandstone between steep bluffs and segments of cliff in Ferruginous Sands. It extends through the upper parts

Above, Fig. 44: Knock Cliff, west of Shanklin, with Sandrock Beds overlying the darker Ferruginous Sands.

Below, Fig. 45: Cliffs cut in the Sandrock Beds in Luccombe Bay, with a grassy ledge on a clay outcrop.

Above, Fig. 46: Luccombe Chine, cut into the Sandrock Beds, the stream flowing across a bench of sandy clay to spill over the lower cliff.
Below, Fig. 47: Slumping Gault over Sandrock at Bordwood Ledge, south of Luccombe Chine. The Needle is a residual column of Sandrock.

of the Ferruginous Sands, down to the Foliated Sand and Clay (Table 3).

A walk along Appley Beach comes under bold Knock Cliff, the lower part showing dark Ferruginous Sands, the upper part massive grey Sandrock Beds capped by yellow bedded sandstones (Fig. 44). Between the upper and lower cliff is a grassy bench on the outcrop of about 2 metres of dark grey impermeable sandy clay, seepage of groundwater from the overlying Sandrock Beds having undermined and caused recession of the upper cliff. The dark lower cliff is generally wet with seepage, and shows frequent slumping, forming basal talus cones that are washed away by waves at high tides. The rock formations dip gently south-west off the Shanklin Anticline, so that a prominent dark green glauconitic clayey sandstone near the base of the cliff, known as the Exogyra Sandstone[66] descends to the foot of Shanklin Point, where it forms a basal bench that widens and runs out to form the intertidal Horse Ledge. Above the Exogyra Beds in the vertical cliff face are stratified grey clayey sandstones, one of which, a thick cross-bedded yellow sandstone, descends to the shore to form Yellow Ledge, about 300 metres south of Horse Ledge. The grassy bench at the top of the lower cliff on dark grey sandy clay also descends to the shore in Luccombe Bay.

At low tide it is possible to walk round Shanklin Point and into Luccombe Bay, where steps lead up through Luccombe Chine to the Coastal Footpath. There are good views of the cliffs and shore features, but the walk should not be attempted when the tide is rising or when the sea is stormy. At Horse Ledge a wooden groyne runs out across the shore, and has trapped a small beach of eastward-drifting cobbles. Beyond this is a sandy cove where the lower cliff of dark Ferruginous Sands has collapsed in a landslide, with fallen boulders of greensand, and on the shore are small structural ledges with scoured pools, the outcrops disintegrating into slabs and boulders.

The sandstones of Yellow Ledge then cross the shore, and a second wooden groyne, with steps, marks the start of Luccombe Bay. The cliffs revive, with the lower cliff in dark basal Sandrock Beds undergoing marine erosion, a grassy bench on the green sandy clay, then upper cliffs cut in the upper part of the Sandrock Beds, a massive pale grey sandstone overlain by layered yellow and white sands (Fig. 45). The recession of these upper cliffs is due to subaerial rather than marine erosion, basal sapping by emerging groundwater, with recurrent slumping, seen in the sandy fans on the grassy and scrubby bench on either side of Luccombe Chine. At the base of the lower cliff are small patches of cobble beach, with some iron-stained brown flints, and sand and bouldery areas exposed on the shore at low tide.

From the shore, Luccombe Chine is seen as a deeply incised wooded ravine cut through the Sandrock Beds of the upper cliffs, the stream cascading down from a broken weir, across the bench on sandy clay to spill over the lower cliff of dark grey sandstone (Fig. 46). A wooden stairway leads up from the shore to a footpath that climbs through the Chine.

It is possible at low tide to clamber over the boulders along the shore south of Luccombe Chine to Bordwood Ledge and on into Steel Bay, but there is a risk of being cut off by the rising tide, or embayed by a stormy sea. The boulders are mainly of greensand, but some are dark and ferruginous, derived from the Carstone high in the cliffs. There are segments of tilted and broken stone and concrete wall, the remains of old cottages that once stood here. The lower cliff of dark sandstone soon disappears beneath an apron of Gault clay that has slumped down over the Sandrock cliffs, and in places there is a cliff up to 2 metres high cut into lobes of this Gault (Fig. 47). At Bordwood Ledge the wide shore is littered with boulders, beneath which are areas of wave-cut ramp in the soft Gault clay and some scoured pools. In Steel Bay the bouldery shore continues in front of slumped Gault and segments of sandstone cliff, the southward-dipping upper Sandrock Beds and Carstone forming a high brown cliff at Dunnose, with blue-grey Gault spilling over its crest to form a basal talus on the backshore. The sea is often muddy here. The Sandrock continues intermittently between sectors of downwash and slumped material, descending to Monk's Bay, where the sharp junction with the overlying red brown Carstone can be seen in the cliffs. The coastline is being cut back as wave action attacks the Carstone cliff and washes away the aprons of slumped material, but the instability of the coastal terrain is due primarily to the effects of percolating groundwater.

It is best to return along the shore, and climb the steps through Luccombe Chine to the Coastal Footpath, which can be followed eastward, back into Shanklin, or westward through the Undercliff to Bonchurch and Ventnor.

The Undercliff: Shanklin to Ventnor

From Appley Beach at the western end of Shanklin seafront the Coastal Footpath turns up Appley Steps to the Rylstone Gardens, then along Luccombe Road to become a track past the Luccombe Tea Rooms. From the top of Knock Cliff the ground rises inland across the Carstone to hummocky, slumped topography on the Gault. The wide perched basin behind Luccombe Bay is floored with Gault, and overlooked by the escarpment of the Upper Greensand and Lower Chalk. Luccombe village is on the northern side of this perched basin, and the Luccombe stream descends steeply into the thickly vegetated Luccombe Chine, cutting down through the Gault and brown Carstone to the pale Sandrock formation.

The Coastal Footpath skirts Luccombe village and is followed across the perched basin on the Gault to pass on the seaward side of the prominent steep-sided spur of Nansen Hill, on the escarpment of Upper Greensand and Lower Chalk. The Undercliff, a broad strip of descending terraces of Chalk and Upper Greensand that have subsided over the Gault, begins here, overlooked by an upper cliff in which layers of Upper Greensand outcrop, overlain by the Lower Chalk. This topography is the outcome of extensive landslides caused by water percolating through the permeable Chalk and Upper Greensand. Water that flows down the seaward-dipping Gault surface emerges as springs and seepages which wash out sediment, undermining the Chalk and Upper Greensand. Thus lubricated, the Gault surface becomes slippery, and from time to time the overlying formations slide seaward.

There were major slides near Bonchurch in 1810, 1818, and again in 1928. The bedded Upper Greensand can be seen by making a detour up to the Devil's Chimney, where the path zig-zags through clefts cut out along joints.

The Landslip Footpath starts at the rhododendron garden and runs through a wooded hummocky, broken and irregular undercliff bench of chalky material, greensand, and blue clay. Towards Dunnose there is active slumping, with many breakaways, subsided terraces, spilling Gault and fallen trees. A steep talus slope of chalk, sandstone and clay extends in places all the way down to the shore. The Coastal Footpath has been frequently disrupted and diverted by slumping, and the muddy Gault is very slippery when wet.

Beyond Dunnose the footpath descends out of woodland to a grassy slope, past Carigdene Farm to Monks Bay, where there are more slipped masses of Chalk and Upper Greensand and areas of broken rubbly terrain. The shore below is divided by blocky groynes, one parallel to the coast with a lee tombolo[67] of shingle and sand. A side track runs down to the Boathouse, and back along the concrete sea wall and boulder groynes which end at Monks Bay. Here the brown Carstone and the underlying yellow and white current-bedded Sandrock can be seen in the cliff, capped by the Gault, but the overlying formations have been disturbed by landslides. To the west the coast is entirely in slumped material, mainly tilted and fractured Lower Chalk and Upper Greensand, the underlying Lower Greensand formations being concealed in the Undercliff past Ventnor, until they reappear in Puckaster Cove below Niton.

Sea walls of varying design have been built westward from Horseshoe Bay to Ventnor, and the Coastal Footpath passes cliffs in slumped material, some of which have been graded to grassy slopes. The sea wall from Bonchurch to Wheelers Bay (Fig. 48) was completed in 1988, and some sectors have been further protected by concrete tetrapods. Groynes have been added in the hope of retaining beaches of flint cobbles and pebbles, and a sandy shore is exposed at low tide with scattered outlying boulders. The coastline has been stabilised, but the whole of the Undercliff east and west of Ventnor remains potentially unstable.

Behind the landslides the upper cliff between Bonchurch and Blackgang is cut into Upper Greensand and Lower Chalk, with strata that appear almost horizontal, but are in fact dipping gently southward. There are vertical cliffs in which chert bands near the top of the Upper Greensand stand out as ledges between grooves cut into intervening softer sands by wind and rain. These are capped by a slope in overlying sandy beds rising to the capping of marly Lower Chalk. This capping forms the brow on the upper cliff from Nansen Hill above Dunnose west beyond St. Lawrence to the Telecom station, and reappears west of the Niton wind gap to crown St. Catherine's Hill, above Blackgang.

Fig. 48: Artificial coast at Bonchurch, where a sea wall has been built in front of slumped masses of Lower Chalk and Upper Greensand.

Ventnor

Ventnor originated as a watering place and spa because of a spring near the base of the slumped cliffs, now seen as a Cascade behind the Esplanade. Below the rockery and gardens is a large model of the Isle of Wight to which geologists will object because of the implication that it is entirely surrounded by white cliffs. The Esplanade is fronted by a sandy beach with splays of fine brown flint and chert shingle, and the town has been built on a series of descending terraces along the Undercliff. These now form a steep, but relatively stable and wooded stairway, overlooked by the escarpment of Upper Greensand crowned with Lower Chalk. The pier, damaged by storms, has been dismantled and removed, and the sea wall comes to an end under the pink Spyglass Inn. The coast to the west is protected by boulder ramparts.

Exploration of the coast from Ventnor to Whale Chine requires some planning. It is possible to follow footpaths along the coast west from the Spyglass Inn as far as Binnel Bay, where it turns inland, up through the Undercliff to Niton, then along the top of the cliffs westward to Blackgang, and down to Whale Chine. Alternatively, it is possible at low tide (and with some difficulty) to walk on along the shore from Binnel Bay to Puckaster Cove, Reeth Bay and St. Catherine's Lighthouse, over to Rocken End, then westward below the Blackgang cliffs to Whale Chine.

Car access to this part of the coast is very restricted. The main road (A3055) runs from Ventnor up to Niton, over to Blackgang and down to Whale Chine. It offers wide views, but sees little of the intervening coastline. It is possible to turn off the A3055 and drive along St. Catherine's Road, west of St Lawrence, to find a footpath down to the lighthouse at St. Catherine's Point. Alternatively, Sandstone Road leads on from here to a car park at Windy Corner, from which a footpath leads down to Rocken End. As noted, it is possible to walk from St. Catherine's Point over to Rocken End, and (at low tide) along the shore from there to Whale Chine, but there is no convenient access to the coast from Blackgang.

Ventnor to Rocken End

The steep coast west from Ventnor consists of wooded slopes on talus and slumped rock, with basal cliffs cut into slipped masses of Chalk and Upper Greensand, often with a landward dip, indicating rotational slumping. The Coastal Footpath climbs the hill past the Spyglass Inn at the end of the Esplanade, and descends into Castle Cove. The cliffs between Ventnor and Castle Cove are armoured with a basal revetment of large (4-6 tonnes) blocks of Carboniferous Limestone imported from the Mendip Hills. These were designed to absorb wave energy and promote beach accretion, but there is very little beach at high tide in front of them. Blue Gault is exposed in the slope beside the concrete path that leads down to Castle Cove, where there is a boat ramp and boulder groynes, the revetment continuing round the cove in front of a concrete Esplanade backed by gabions and a landscaped slope. The coastline is thus artificial, and of no interest geologically or geomorphologically.

An older sea wall runs round the point into Steephill Cove, which contains a small beach. Steps lead up a steep bluff to the Undercliff, where the subsided Greensand is tilted, so that a coastal ridge is backed by a wide hollow containing a cricket ground, and then the Botanical Gardens. The Coastal Footpath runs westward along the top of the lower cliff, past Orchard Bay, in which cliffs of slumped Upper Greensand overlook a bouldery shore with a sand and shingle beach, backed by Orchard Bay House. The cliff crest undulates, backed by the wide hollow which contains the Rare Breeds Farm, and has been cut into behind Sir Richard Cove. There is a sharp rise to Woody Point, a steeply cliffed scrubby coastal ridge (Fig. 49).

The Undercliff is here about 600 metres wide, backed by a partly forested escarpment in which there are segments of cliff showing stratified Upper Greensand beneath the capping Lower Chalk, which can be seen to fade out westward towards Niton. Although there have been massive landslides here in the past, the Undercliff in the St. Lawrence area is now fairly stable, although subsidence still continues to affect the A3055 and to cause structural problems in buildings.

The Coastal Footpath descends from Woody Point and has been diverted behind the cottages at Woody Bay, where the former footpath was cut away by cliff recession. A side track runs down into Woody Bay, a cove with a shingle beach, and cliffs about 10 metres high in back-tilted Upper Greensand. The Coastal Footpath turns inland at Woody Bay, but a cliff-top footpath continues, skirting another cliffed scrubby knoll, and passes several jagged outcrops of tilted Upper Greensand, above cliffs that descend to a bouldery shore. Towards Binnel Point are craggy cliffs up to 15 metres high and irregular knolls of subsided

Above, Fig. 49: Woody Point, a knoll of subsided and tilted Upper Greensand on the coast south of St. Lawrence. Below, Fig 50: A low cliff in slumped Chalk and upper Greensand at Binnel Bay fronts the wide Undercliff west of St. Lawrence, behind which is a cliff of Upper Greensand, capped by Lower Chalk.

Upper Greensand (Fig. 50). Ahead the lighthouse on St. Catherine's Point comes into view.

The cliffs decline behind Binnel Bay as the broad backing hollow reaches the coast, and a long densely vegetated slope develops, with landslides descending to the shore. The beach consists of cobbles and pebbles of flint and sandstone, with patches of brown flint sand and grit, and sandy areas are exposed at low tide. It is backed by slumping low bluffs of Gault with subsiding sandstone boulders (Fig. 51). There are segments of an old masonry wall, about 20 metres offshore, relics of an attempt to stabilise this part of the coastline.

Fig. 51: Slumping Gault on the coast of Binnel Bay is fronted by a beach of flint cobbles, with boulders of Upper Greensand and Sandrock.

At this point (524757) the footpath turns inland up clay steps through tamarisk scrub, and climbs through the Undercliff to St. Lawrence. It may be wise to detour inland here, but it is possible at low tide to scramble along the shore to Puckaster Cove and round to Reeth Bay and Castle Haven, where the cliff-top footpath resumes. There are bouldery salients between small coves with shingle and sand beaches in front of the low crumbling bluffs of Gault, and wet muddy patches where rivulets cross the shore. Brown sand and fragments of brown and grey sandstone indicate that the landslides have incorporated material from the Carstone and the Sandrock Beds, but the outcrops are hidden by the wide landslides.

In the western part of Binnel Bay the coastal slope steepens, and there are storm-piled cobble beaches in front of a crumbling bluff. This passes laterally into a cliff in layered grey-green Sandrock, over which landslides of Gault clay and sandstone debris are locally spilling. The cliff crest is backed by a gently rising slope. Little caves and clefts have been cut out along joints in the Sandrock, and the cliff is fronted by a bouldery shore, with large blocks of Upper Greensand and some dark brown fragments of ferruginous gritty Carstone. The cliffs run out to a small headland, with a few poles marking former defensive structures, and a slumping bluff with light brown sandstone boulders in a clay matrix.

Round this point is Reeth Bay, in which cliffs of soft blue-grey sandstone stand vertically behind a shelving sandy beach which is completely submerged at high tide (Fig. 52). There are the remains of an old stone wall and boat ramp, partly buried by a clayey landslide. The bouldery shore resumes, with small ferruginous pebbles from a cliff base outcrop of ferruginous sandstone and conglomerate, to Castle Haven, where a boat ramp is protected by groynes of boulders confined between wooden poles. Behind is a slate-roofed cottage, and a gravelly lane leading up to a barn at the Castlehaven Caravan Site.

Fig. 52: Cliffs cut in the Sandrock Beds behind a sandy beach at Reeth Bay, looking west towards St. Catherine's Point.

This point is also accessible by way of a track leading down from St. Catherine's Road (p. 102). A cliff-top footpath (signposted Watershoot Bay) runs through the caravan site and into the National Trust property, Knowles Farm, with its stone walls bounding large fields around St. Catherine's Lighthouse. The cliffs are 6 to 8 metres high, cut in rubbly Chalk and bouldery Upper Greensand, with Gault clay outcropping locally in the cliff base and on the boulder-strewn shore. Active cliff recession is indicated by calving, subsidence and rock falls. St. Catherine's Lighthouse stands in a walled enclosure extending back from the cliff across a low coastal terrace, behind which the Undercliff rises in steps to St. Catherine's Road and Sandstone Road, where it is overlooked by a steep grassy and scrubby escarpment of Upper Greensand.

West of the Lighthouse the terrace becomes broken and hummocky, with knolls and hollows, tors and craggy outcrops of Upper Greensand. Along the coast, Highdown and The Needles come into view. The footpath descends into Watershoot Bay, a cove with large boulders of Chalk and Upper Greensand into which a stream descends through a rushy swamp between grassy hummocks of Gault. The landslides then become higher and more irregular on the collapsing promontory that runs down to Rocken End, and pathways lead round through the rocky debris to the cove where the Lower Greensand cliffs begin. There is a view on past Blackgang, along Chale Bay to Atherfield Point, Brighstone Bay, Hanover Point, and Compton Bay, with the Chalk cliffs on either side of Freshwater Bay.

Above Rocken End the irregular landslide topography ascends to the base of Gore Cliff, and there is a footpath link with the car park at Windy Corner, at the end of Sandstone Road. Gore Cliff (Fig. 8) is a vertical upper cliff in evenly-bedded horizontally stratified Upper Greensand, with protruding ledges of hard nodular cornstones and etched out shelves in softer sandstone which are much frequented by birds. It is capped by the Lower Chalk, which forms a receded brow behind a wind-scoured bench. The Upper Greensand is underlain by the dark Gault, and it is again the intervening seepage zone that has been responsible for the upper cliff recession and subsiding landslides, seepage and outflow having lubricated the junction between the Gault clay and the overlying sandstones, washing out sediment and causing seaward slumping and sliding. There was a major landslide here in 1799, and subsidence has continued intermittently.

At Windy Corner the old undercliff road that led to Blackgang has been breached as the result of subsidence. A well-known sketch of this road appears in the Geological Memoir[68], showing Gore Cliff (Lower Chalk over layered chert beds over freestones over sandstone with concretions) above a field with a lane bordered by an already irregular fence, and a lady with a parasol, but much of this disappeared during a major landslide in 1928. From Windy Corner a rough footpath can be followed across this landslide, crossing ridges and gullies of sandstone and clay, in places thickly vegetated, through to the remains of the old road to Blackgang.

Alternatively, it is possible to go back to Niton and find the Coastal Footpath by walking up Boxers Lane and out on to the crest of the cliffs by the radio station. The upper escarpment passes into Gore Cliff, and there are good views down across the Undercliff to St. Catherine's Point with the Lighthouse, Watershoot Bay and Rocken End. Ahead is the broad view along Chale Bay, with the Chalk cliffs of Compton Bay in the distance, and to the right the slopes of Niton Down rise towards St. Catherine's Hill, 236 metres above sea level. The Coastal Footpath comes to the end of Gore Cliff, overlooking Blackgang, where the wooded area above the high Lower Greensand cliffs is occupied by an amusement park. The Upper Greensand escarpment then runs inland, and steps descend to the Blackgang car park. There is a bus service back from here to Ventnor.

Rocken End to Whale Chine

At low tide it is possible to walk from Rocken End along the beach (just over 2 miles) to Whale Chine, the next point where the shore is accessible from the land. North-west from the stream mouth at Rocken End the slumping Gault and Upper Greensand give place to a much bolder slope as the underlying Lower Greensand formations emerge, the dark brown Carstone above the paler Sandrock beds. The cliffs steepen and increase in height towards Blackgang, behind a beach of fine reddish-brown flint shingle and sand. There are many heaps of talus resulting from rock falls.

About 180 metres north-west of Rocken End the Ferruginous Sands formation appears at the base of an almost vertical cliff, and rises westward (Fig. 53). Another 450 metres along the shore this cliff swings landward beneath Blackgang to form a high, vertical upper cliff behind a widening terrace that declines seaward to a lower cliff overlooking the beach. Gault clay is spilling over the Carstone and the massive Sandrock beds which outcrop in the upper 60 metres of Blackgang Cliff. A century ago there was a deep, narrow V-shaped Blackgang Chine incised through these formations into the underlying Ferruginous Sands, with the stream cascading over the hard Ferruginous Bands (Fig. 20), but this has been almost completely removed by cliff recession during successive landslides. There is now only a broad cliffed re-entrant, with a truncated road and drainpipes marking the head of the former chine and the site of the

Above, Fig. 53: Rocken End, where the slumping Undercliff gives place to cliffs cut in Sandrock and Ferruginous Sands, rising westward to Blackgang. The upper cliff of Chert Beds is visible on the right   Below, Fig. 54: The cliffs at Blackgang (site of the former Chine), where the Sandrock Beds and Sands of Walpen Undercliff dominate the receding upper cliff, fronted by a terrace on the impermeable Foliated Clay and Sand.

Above, Fig. 55: A view of the Undercliff terrace rising westward from Blackgang, as seen from the cliff-top near Chale.

Below, Fig. 56: Ladder Chine (left) and Walpen Chine (right) notch the top of the cliffs cut in the Walpen and Ladder Sands, underlain by darker Walpen Clay and Sand to the east of Whale Chine.

commercialised Dinosaur Park. Recurrent landslides have damaged and destroyed cottages and chalets at Blackgang.

In describing the cliffs of Chale Bay it is useful to refer to the subdivisions of the Ferruginous Sands originally defined by Dr W.H. Fitton in 1845 (Table 3), which outcrop in sequence along the cliffs westward to Atherfield Point. The nomenclature is cumbersome and a little repetitive, but is still used in geological reports. First come the Ferruginous Bands of Blackgang Chine, about 6 metres of coherent brown and yellow sands and massive sandstones which rise from the shore to form a vertical cliff below the Sandrock beds, ascending towards Blackgang, where they used to outcrop in a waterfall in the chine. Below these are about 30 metres of thick brown, green and white sandstones, also forming vertical cliffs, and known as the Sands of Walpen Undercliff. They rise to dominate the upper cliff west of the site of Blackgang Chine (Fig. 54), along towards Walpen Chine, 180 metres short of which where they disappear at the top of the cliff.

These high cliffs overlook an undercliff terrace up to 130 metres wide, covered with slumped debris and sandy outwash fans (Fig. 21). This has developed on the outcrop of the Foliated Clay and Sand, a laminated green sand and dark blue clay 7.5 metres thick. At the top issue springs and seepages of groundwater from the thick overlying sandstones, especially after wet weather. Lubrication and outwash by this seepage has been has been responsible for the undermining, collapse and recession of the high backing sandstone cliffs, and the consequent disappearance of Blackgang Chine. The undercliff terrace on these laminated beds rises and narrows towards the cliff crest on the eastern side of Walpen Chine (Fig. 55).

The instability of the cliffs bordering Chale Bay has been due to undercutting of the Ferruginous Sands by stormy seas on a coast exposed to south-westerly gales. The undercliff terrace ends seaward in a steep, locally vertical, lower cliff cut into the Cliff End Sand. This cliff gradually increases in height as the Cliff End Sand rises westward, and the underlying green sands and clays of the Upper Gryphaea Beds and the homogeneous grey-green Walpen and Ladder Sands emerge in succession and rise through the cliff face. A basal ledge then appears on the outcrop of the doggers (large concretions of calcareous sandstone) at the top of the Upper Crioceras Beds. This ledge also rises westward, then fades out. Another basal ledge then appears the on dark Walpen Clay and Sand, with strong seepage of groundwater from the overlying sands, and this rises until it is cut through by Whale Chine.

West of Blackgang Chine the crest of the upper cliff declines gradually to Walpen Chine and Ladder Chine, two truncated and hanging valleys cut into the Walpen and Ladder Sands (Fig. 56). Sketches made by Dr. Fitton a century and a half ago (Fig. 57) show that they were then cut more deeply into the cliffs, Walpen Chine extending down almost to sea level, Ladder Chine with a deep slot cut down into the Upper Crioceras Beds, but cliff recession has greatly reduced them in comparison with Whale Chine, which has been maintained by its down-cutting stream.

The shore walk ends at Whale Chine, where steps lead up to the car park.

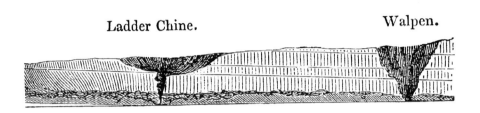

Fig. 57: Ladder Chine and Walpen Chine as they were in the 1840s (from a sketch by W.H. Fitton[14]). Compare Fig. 56.

Ventnor to Whale Chine by road

The A3055 from Ventnor climbs through the Niton col and over the Chalk ridge to Blackgang. As the road winds down the escarpment there is a long view westward over Chale Bay and along the cliffed coast to Atherfield Point and the little salient near Nodes, on to the Chalk ridge at Compton Down, and beyond that Tennyson Down. This is the Tennyson Heritage Coast, an Area of Outstanding Natural Beauty and a Site of Special Scientific Interest. The Military Road runs behind the cliffs through to Whale Chine.

Alternatively, there is a footpath from Blythe Chute at Chale, down across fields to the cliffs, where it is possible (taking great care, as these cliffs are dangerous) to look down on the Blackgang Undercliff, a reedy terrace rising westward. A stream flows out of a ditch and descends a small chine, Chale Chine, at an angle to the cliff crest. The footpath continues along the top of the cliffs, with good views towards Atherfield Point, and a small valley develops behind a jagged sandstone outcrop, parallel to the coast, then turns to descend Walpen Chine, cut in yellow-brown Cliff End Sand.

Further on is Ladder Chine, with a broader cliff-top hollow, a smooth sandstone slope scoured by wind action, in the grey Walpen and Ladder Sands.

It is possible to look down on the bench that forms and rises westward, across Whale Chine, narrowing as it ascends the cliffs.

On this part of the coast the cliffs are capped by up to 2 metres of blown sand, which may have been winnowed from the sandy Lower Greensand cliffs and the beach, and blown up on to the cliff crest, but this process is now confined to small areas at the top of Walpen Chine and Ladder Chine. There is none of the cliff-top dune topography, diminishing inland, usually seen in such situations, and it is more likely that this horizontal capping of wind-blown sand (which contains much silt) originated as a brickearth, winnowed from hinterland outcrops of Ferruginous Sands during a Late Pleistocene cold phase when there was little or no vegetation (p. 25). Indeed, similar fine-grained sediment is winnowed from ploughed fields in this area during dry weather when strong winds produce clouds of red dust.

The footpath then runs inland to the Military Road, and so to the car park above Whale Chine.

Whale Chine to Shepherd's Chine

It is possible to walk along the beach from Whale Chine to Shepherd's Chine, a distance of about two miles, when the tide is low. Steps lead down into Whale Chine, which has been deeply incised into the coastal plateau, between cliffs cut in Ferruginous Sands (Upper Crioceras Beds, underlain by the Walpen Clay and Sand), dipping about 3° ESE (see cover photograph) These cliffs are capped with an earthy flint and chert gravel and up to a metre of wind-blown sand. The gravel occupied the floor of an older, wider and gentler valley, into which the modern chine became incised as the result of stream downcutting induced by cliff recession. The upper valley is only slightly incised, and occupied by dense scrub, but it deepens and widens to become a cliff-sided chine, down which flows a stream (a former dam has collapsed) which crosses a hard band in the Walpen Clay and Sand as a waterfall, then descends over boulders to the shingle beach (Fig. 58). The beach is of brown flinty coarse sand, granules and small pebbles, derived partly from sandstone outcrops in the cliffs and on the sea floor, and partly from the cliff-top gravels. The top of the Lower Crioceras Beds forms ledges off the mouth of Whale Chine.

West of Whale Chine the hard dark clay band seen in the waterfall forms a bench in the cliff face, strewn with yellow and brown sand and clay derived from the Upper Crioceras beds in the surmounting cliff. The bench rises westward, narrowing as the hard band approaches the top of the cliff. It is underlain by green and grey mudstones of the Lower Crioceras Beds and the

Scaphites Beds, and about 300 metres to the north-west the red and brown sandstones of the Lower Gryphaea Beds form a ledge which also rises from beach level and ascends the cliff.

Fig; 58: Whale Chine, cut into the Upper Crioceras Beds, with the dark Walpen Clay towards the base. See also the Cover photograph.

On the walk along to Atherfield Point the cliff becomes bolder on the outcrop of the underlying Crackers Group, which comprises yellow-brown sandy clays underlain by 6 metres of compact grey and brown sand with two prominent layers of large rounded tabular calcareous sandstone concretions. They form bands ascending the cliff face towards Atherfield Point.

Next to emerge in the base of the cliff is the Atherfield Clay, about 30 metres of unstratified light blue (weathering to brown) silty clay, which has collapsed into small talus cones along the back of the beach. The cliff profile declines into a 30°-40° slope as the Atherfield Clay rises to dominate it, and there is a clay undercliff bench, on to which boats are hauled. The Atherfield Clay disintegrates into sharp angular fragments in the numerous slumped talus cones behind the beach of fine shingle.

Atherfield Point is a steep cliff of crumbling silty clay (Fig. 7) that protrudes because there is a reef of calcareous sandstone, the Perna Bed, exposed at low tide on the shore. The dip is gentle, about 3° SSE. The Perna Bed, an iron-stained calcareous sandstone about a metre thick, appears in the cliff base at Atherfield Point. It then rises to the top of the cliff about 270 metres south-east of Shepherd's Chine.

West of Atherfield Point the base of the cliff shows outcrops of laminated mudstones, the Vectis Shales (Fig. 59). These appear beneath the Perna Bed, and the junction can be seen rising in the cliffs until it reaches the crest about 600 metres west of the Point. The Vectis Shales here consist of about 58 metres of dull blue to black mudstones, with some sandstones, occasional ironstones, and thin dark limestone beds. The mudstones form ledges that rise gently westward and disintegrate into platy slabs. An upper cliff with a vertical gravel capping recedes behind slumped clay, truncated by a wave-cut lower cliff.

Fig. 59: Mudstones in the Vectis Shales Formation (Wealden) east of Shepherd's Chine.

Shepherd's Chine, cut in the soft Vectis Shales, is wider in cross profile than Whale Chine, with gentle grassy slopes showing some slumping, an intact dam, and gabions along the stream bank. The meandering stream opens to a brown beach of mainly small flint pebbles, and the steeply sloping cliffs on either side show bedded grey and brown Vectis Shales dipping gently south-eastward on the northern limb of the Brighstone Anticline, back towards Atherfield Point. The cliffs are about 30 metres high, capped by earthy gravels. Early in the 19th century Atherfield Brook flowed to the sea through Cowleaze Chine, 320 metres to the north-west, but around 1820 it was intercepted by a cliff gully cutting back into its valley. The capture was possibly assisted by a shepherd who dug a ditch through a narrow ridge of shale to divert the stream, hence Shepherd's Chine, which has subsequently deepened and widened its valley, while Cowleaze Chine has been left high and dry.

A track leads up through Shepherd's Chine, and the cliff-top footpath may be taken back to Whale Chine.

Shepherd's Chine to Grange Chine

This is a shore walk of about two miles, best commenced when the tide is falling. At the mouth of Shepherd's Chine the beach is of flint pebbles, and a low tide ledge of grey, yellow and red shelly sandstone within the Vectis Shales is exposed on the shore (Fig. 60). About 100 metres to the north-west this appears behind the beach as a wall of massive sandstone 3 to 5 metres thick in the base of the cliff, ascending to the west. It outcrops on either side of Cowleaze Chine, a short hanging valley[69], and continues to rise until it forms a bold breakaway at the top of the cliff at Barnes High, more than 50 metres above sea level (Fig. 61) It is known as the Sandstone of Barnes High.

The cliff-top footpath north-west from Cowleaze Chine ascends to Barnes High, where the massive sandstone forms a small but prominent west-facing escarpment (Fig. 6) that curves inland from the cliff crest a short way, fading round the coastal hill. There are numerous cracks parallel to the cliff crest, along which subsidence occurs from time to time, resulting in upper cliff recession.

Below the Sandstone of Barnes High the upper part of the steeply sloping cliff is cut into the pink and grey Vectis Shales. A small bench on a thin hard greenish silty band with much lignite marks the rising top of the underlying Wessex Formation, which consists of red, purple and green marls with thin beds of mud-cracked sandstone and sandy limestone.

Just west of Barnes High there is a prominent lobe of slumped gravelly clay. The shingle beach becomes higher and wider, with berm terraces. The cliff crest drops sharply as the Barnes High Sandstone comes to an end, but Barnes Chine, 150 metres to the west, is no more than a notch in the cliff. By now the Wessex Marls have risen to occupy the whole of the cliff face, and they form the cliffs for more than three miles westward to Brook Bay.

Ship Ledge, along the shore from Barnes High, is an outcrop of fine white sandstone, and to the north-west a second one appears. These two harder horizons form vertical walls rising through the cliffs, which steepen towards

Above, Fig. 60: The Barnes High Sandstone (part of the Vectis Formation) emerging at the cliff base west of Shepherd's Chine, and rising north-westward
Below, Fig. 61: The Barnes High Sandstone at the crest of the cliff west of Cowleaze Chine, underlain by Vectis Shales, with the Wessex Marls below the sandstone band.

Nodes, where the cliff crest is sharp-edged. At the base of the beach a shore platform of red and grey knobbly sandstone appears, covered with seaweed, that is exposed at low tide. This is responsible for the slight salient in the cliffs at Nodes, where there is a cliff-top dry valley between two summits.

Beyond Nodes the beach becomes sandy, and there is a gently-sloping cliff cut in red and grey Wessex Marls. There are some outcrops of red and grey sandstone at the foot of the beach and at the cliff base, bold crags at the cliff top as each sandstone band arrives, and a gentler profile on the marls. To the north-west the Grange Chine Black Band is seen in the cliff, a conspicuous grey silty clay.

The cliff crest drops sharply on either side of Grange Chine, where it is less than 20 metres high at the head of a slight embayment. Grange Chine, joined by Marsh Chine below the brick bridge on the Military Road, is incised into this valley, between cliffs cut into red and green marls, capped by a vertical wall of gravel up to a metre high. The bordering slopes are scrubby, with some slumping, and the stream descends to pass below a footbridge and flow through a shingle beach.

A track leads up from the footbridge to the Military Road at Grange Farm, and the Coastal Footpath runs back along the cliff top to Shepherd's Chine.

Grange Chine to Brook Chine

This is a walk of about 2.5 miles along the shore at low tide. The cliff crest undulates between 15 and 30 metres high west of Grange Chine, forming a steep slope in the Wessex Marls, and showing a series of half saucer-shaped depressions in the upper part of the cliff. These become larger past the Brighstone Holiday Centre cabins, where the cliff crest is scalloped above a subsided undercliff of varying width. To the north-west is Chilton Chine, with a winding stream in a narrow scrubby ravine cut into pink and grey marls. A footpath and wooden steps descend to the shore on the western side, the stream flowing to a sand and pebble beach. The Chilton Chine Sandstone ascends at about 5° from the beach immediately east of the chine, forming a bench on either side of the incised valley as it coarsens and thickens westward. This bench formed as the result of the washing away of overlying grey silty clay.

The cliffs to the north-west of Chilton Chine are cut in the variegated red, brown, grey and purple Wessex Marls, with minor headlands, especially where occasional beds of white, red, pink or yellow sandstone outcrop at the cliff base. A pink sandstone band forms an intertidal reef off a small cape just west of Chilton Chine, one of the sites where dinosaur footprints (120 million years old) have been seen on ripple-marked bedding-planes exposed at low tide. This is the Sudmoor Point Sandstone, and 500 metres to the west its base is seen in the bottom of the cliff, rising over purple and red mottled mudstones.

To the north-west a shore platform of knobbly red sandstone in front of the shelving sandy beach extends along the coast as far as Brook Chine. The massive Sudmoor Point Sandstone up to 5 metres thick, forms a bold feature in the cliff below slopes of pale grey and pink marl, and along the coast this rises in the cliff face, above cracking red marls (Fig. 62). There are small salients of fallen blocks of grey and brown gritstone and conglomerate. In places there are ramps of red sandstone behind the grey sandy beach, rising to the base of the cliff. The strata are almost horizontal, but there is a slight landward dip which, intersected by a broad bay, appears to form a syncline in the cliffs. The cliff crest runs along the seaward side of a broad Sudmoor valley that descends gently north-westward to Brook.

Fig. 62: The Sudmoor Point Sandstone in the Wessex Formation north-west of Chilton Chine. This sandstone formed in a meandering river channel, and is overlain by former flood-plain clays.

Along the shore the massive sandstone is seen half way up the cliff at Sudmoor Point (393827), where it divides into several thinner beds with intervening marly horizons to the north-west underlain by red marls and overlain by red and green marls. This sequence has been interpreted as sandy channel deposits of a river meandering on an aggrading muddy flood-plain in Cretaceous times (p. 26). There is a small promontory on a slight flexure in the sandstone, which is also seen in the truncated bedding down on the shore platform. Beyond this, in the absence of the sandstone, the cliff declines into a slumping bluff in Wessex Marls.

Along this part of the coast there is Sudmoor Undercliff (395826), a terrace 50 to 150 metres wide, backed by a gravel-capped upper cliff which increases in height to more than 33 metres at Sudmoor Point. The cliff crest is scalloped, overlooking a series of arcuate depressions where the Wessex Marls have subsided (Fig. 63). West of the small promontory is Roughland (388832), a 500 metre long undercliff, backed by a gravel-capped upper cliff up to 200 metres inland, with a lower cliff is 20-25 metres high. The upper cliff is fronted by subsided and tilted blocks and broken ridges where marls have collapsed to form a hummocky terrace with scrubby vegetation, mainly gorse. Towards Brook Chine these landslides come to an end and the gravel-capped upper cliff forms a salient above steep, slumping slopes. The gravelly cap, with some brickearth, is calving away at the cliff crest, and slumped angular gravel has been shaped by wave action into cusps on the sandy beach. There is also a band of dark ferruginous sand on the upper beach, probably derived from the Carstone in Compton Bay, and drifted along the shore.

Fig. 63: Cliff-crest calving behind the subsiding Wessex Marls north-west of Sudmoor Point.

120

The bold cliffs decline to less than 10 metres at the mouth of the Brook valley. Brook Chine is a double chine with converging incised streams between slopes cut in Wessex Marls, and the shore platform is interrupted in a sector where the valley formerly ran out below sea level.

A footpath leads up to the car park beside the Military Road, and the cliff-top footpath returns to Grange Chine, with good views of the upper cliff and the landslides.

Brook Chine to Compton Bay

From Brook Chine it is possible to walk along the shore at low tide in front of cliffs with Brickearth and gravel over bluish Wessex Marls behind a dark sandy beach. There is a section where red marls have apparently filled an earlier furrow in the shales. The cliffs continue past a small chine with a waterfall, out to Hanover Point. The Wessex Marls still dip ESE, and a pink and white current-bedded sandstone rises to form a shore platform, with reefs dipping landward off the Brighstone Anticline.

The Hanover Point cliffs are of fracturing blue clay, capped by earthy gravel and terrace beds (Fig. 64). The Wessex Marls here consist of about 30 metres of red, purple and blue clay with lenticles of sandstone, underlain by grey clay, the lower part of which contains many flat slabs of black lignite. This in turn rests upon about 2 metres of hard grey and pink sandstone seen at the base of Hanover Point and on the outlying intertidal reefs, the formation responsible for the protrusion of this small headland. Embedded in the lower part of this Hanover Point Sandstone are fossil trunks of coniferous trees, scattered in various directions and broken into fragments, which has led to this outcrop being called the Pine Raft[70]. At the lowest spring tides the Pine Raft is seen to overlie variegated marls, which are the lowest beds found in the Wessex Formation, and thus the oldest rocks outcropping in the Isle of Wight. There is a prominent concrete sea mark on the reefs offshore.

The Wessex Marls dip north in the cliffs at Hanover Point, and along the coast to Shippard's Chine the descending beds are seen in sequence up to the base of the Vectis Shales. The cliffs are cut first into red and purple marls, then a pale grey sandstone, overlain by grey clay with lignite, descends the cliff to the beach, and runs out across the shore as a weedy reef. This is followed by more sloping cliffs in purple and variegated clays, then a second pale grey sandstone. Just before Shippard's Chine is a third sandstone and beyond the chine a pink sandstone, each in turn descending to the shore. At Shippard's Chine the car park has been partly lost as the result of cliff recession (Fig. 65).

121

Above, Fig. 64: The Wessex Marls in the cliffs at Hanover Point, fronted by an intertidal ledge of sandstone which includes the Pine Raft.

Below, Fig 65: Slumping in the Wessex Marls at Shippard's Chine has removed part of the car park.

Along the shore north-west of Shippard's Chine the topmost Wessex Beds, purple marls with a grey-green capping silty band, can be seen dipping north-westward below the blue Vectis Shales. The cliffs behind the beach are then cut in Vectis Shales with some interstratified sands, extending to a small ravine about 320 metres west of Shippard's Chine.

Beyond this the outcrops have been much obscured by recurrent slumping, but the shales become contorted, and end at a fault which brings up the purple and red marls Wessex Marls, seen in occasional cliff outcrops and intervening slumped aprons. The shore ledges fade out, and a wide sandy beach is exposed at low tide. The Vectis Shales reappear in the upper cliff, and are thinner, with fewer sandstone beds, than on the coast south of Shippard's Chine. As they are less coherent, the cliff becomes a slumping slope, and recedes behind a wide landslide area in which the Wealden Beds, together with the overlying Atherfield Clay, have collapsed in a broad amphitheatre. The upper cliff begins to rise as it intersects the escarpment of the overlying Ferruginous Sands (the Military Road goes through a cutting in which these sandstones are exposed a little way inland), and a footpath leads up beside a red lifebelt post on the lower cliff, climbing the upper cliff to join the Coastal Footpath above Compton Bay. As the Ferruginous Sands descend northward to the shore the landslides come to an end, and the upper cliff curves round to merge with the lower cliff in a wall of red sandstone 30 metres high.

Those who want to return to Brook Chine may do so by way of the cliff-top footpath.

Compton Bay

Across the road from the car park (371852) near Compton Farm a footpath leads to the stairway at the western end of the Compton Bay landslide and so down to the shore. Crumbling slopes of Atherfield Clay are fronted at low tide by a wide sandy beach. To the north-west are high cliffs in the thick Ferruginous Sands, deeply weathered brown sandstones with many irregular bands of ironstone dipping northward at about 40° (Fig. 66). The subdivisions charted by Fitton in the cliffs between Blackgang and Atherfield Point (Table 3) are not clearly defined on this northern limb of the Brighstone Anticline. The Ferruginous Sands form steep (70°-80°) cliffs up to 60 metres high, declining as the Compton Farm valley comes to the coast. They are overlain by the Sandrock Beds, mainly unconsolidated white quartzose sands interbedded with thin dark grey clays in wavy strata from which there is much seepage. A quartzite pebble bed descends steeply through the cliffs and marks the base of the overlying

Above, Fig. 66: Cliffs cut in Ferruginous Sands, dipping beneath Sandrock, Carstone and Gault to the Upper Greensand and Chalk in Compton Bay.

Below, Fig. 67: View from Compton Chine of the Upper Greensand and Chalk cliffs extending to Freshwater Bay on the left.

Carstone, which in turn passes up into the Gault. There have been several rock falls, and there are minor beaches of gravel lining the cliff base.

The Compton Farm valley has only a small stream falling over the cliffs through Compton Chine, which has been truncated by cliff recession and is now only a small notch in the top of the cliff. The cliff crest drops to about 10 metres across the mouth of this valley, the axis of which follows the outcrop of the Gault, a dark blue silty clay which also dips at about 40° northward through the cliff. The outcrop is also marked by a cliff re-entrant, and is much obscured by vegetation and slumping. A cauldron has been excavated in the cliff face by seepage and runoff. To the west of the Gault the cliff steepens as it is cut through the transitional beds, stratified buff silt and dark blue sandy clays, leading up into the Upper Greensand where the escarpment of the Central Downs intersects the coastline, swinging west-north-westward.

The northward dip increases to more than 50°. The convex south-facing grassy escarpment slope has been undercut by the sea to form steep cliffs on the northern side of Compton Bay, which descend to a shore littered with chalk and greensand boulders. They are best seen from the top of the Ferruginous Sands cliff in Compton Bay, or back from Fort Redoubt on the western side of Freshwater Bay.

The formations exposed in the cliffs along the north shore of Compton Bay include the Upper Greensand, buff and pale green silts and fine sandstones, with chert beds outcropping at the cliff base, declining gradually westward (Fig. 67). The top of the Upper Greensand forms a small promontory, awash at high tide. The Upper Greensand is capped by marly Lower Chalk strata which come down to the shore. The Lower Chalk dips northward at 45° in the basal cliff and narrow foreshore, and consists of dark green Glauconitic Marl, then grey marls and white limestones. At the top of the Lower Chalk are the Plenus Marls, and there is a small promontory where the rough nodular Melbourn Rock outcrops at the base of the layered and hard brittle frost-shattered Middle Chalk. At low tide it is possible can get along the base of the cliffs to see the Middle Chalk, a massive limestone without flints and some bedded nodular and conglomeratic rock, but it is then necessary to turn back, as there is no access along the shore round to Freshwater Bay, even at low tide.

The Chalk cliffs extend towards Freshwater Bay. There is another small promontory on a bed of nodular chalk with flints at the base of the Upper Chalk, which comes in at the top of the cliff west of Compton Bay and descends to the shore near the former Arch Rock, on the eastern side of Freshwater Bay. The northward dip in the Upper Chalk steepens to between 60° and 70°.

Freshwater Bay

Freshwater Bay is a broad cove cut into the upper part of the Western Yar valley where this had previously formed a gap through the Central Downs, much like the river gaps of the Medina at Newport and the Eastern Yar at Brading. It is a semi-circular bay, a little reminiscent of Lulworth Cove in Dorset, but with a wider entrance, and cut entirely in Chalk; it also resembles Arish Mell Gap[71]. The eastern half of the cove has a beach of flint shingle in front of cliffs cut in shattered Upper Chalk, the flint layers having been much disturbed by frost heaving and lateral sludging This is overlain by Coombe Rock and a reddish brown Brickearth (Fig. 68). A walk along the beach to the eastern end of the cove comes to an Upper Chalk cliff where the capping Brickearth has subsided into deep, narrow cylindrical hollows formed by solution of the chalk, and known as soil pipes. Some are several metres long, with dark brown patches where they are intersected by the receding cliffs. There are residual stacks, Stag Rock, Mermaid Rock and the foundations of Arch Rock, on the shore platform below the cliff to the east. Arch Rock (Fig. 23) collapsed during a storm on 25th October 1992. There is a triangular cave in the steeply dipping Upper Chalk.

Fig. 68: Cliffs in frost-shattered Upper Chalk and Coombe Rock, with a capping of Brickearth, Freshwater Bay.

The western half of the bay has a concrete sea wall and promenade running round in front of the Freshwater Bay Hotel. A century ago the beach was depleted by the extraction of shingle to make concrete for Fort Redoubt and other defences, thereby diminishing the shingle barrier that had protected the gap at the head of the Western Yar valley. This was overwashed by waves during a southerly gale in 1905, and there was a risk that a permanent breach might form, separating the western peninsula of the Isle of Wight as 'the Isle of Freshwater'. The concrete sea walls were built to prevent this. To the west the hard Upper Chalk forms rising cliffs above a bouldery, irregular shore platform with a few small stacks and boulders, and there are caves in the Upper Chalk, here dipping northward at about 70°.

Watcombe Bay to The Needles

The Coastal Footpath climbs past Fort Redoubt (344855), along the top of cliffs cut in smooth nodular Upper Chalk which curve round and descend into Watcombe Bay (343856), a small cove cut into the head of a dry valley, a headwater tributary of the Western Yar. Again there is gravelly Coombe Rock in the cliff at the head of the bay, indicating that a deeper valley was excavated, then infilled with frost-shattered chalk and flint sludged down the bordering slopes under periglacial conditions in the Late Pleistocene. The Coombe Rock is overlain by loamy Brickearth. On either side the cliffs are cut into smooth steeply-dipping massive Upper Chalk with regular layers of flint nodules, some tabular (Fig. 69). A gently-shelving shore platform is exposed at low tide.

Between Watcombe Bay and Scratchell's Bay the south-facing cliffs are below the steep convex grassy escarpment that rises to Tennyson Down. It is difficult to see the cliffs from the footpath along the overlying grassy slope: they are best seen from a boat or from the air. They consist of Upper Chalk with bands of flint over a basal outcrop of Middle Chalk dipping north at about 45°, undercut by marine erosion. There are steep noses or ribs of chalk, fans of chalky talus, and many small caves etched out along bedding planes. The cliff crest rises to a point near the Tennyson Monument (325854), then descends across a broad coombe at Highdown Cliff before rising again along the undercut escarpment of West Highdown Hill to Main Bench (303846). It then descends to the low promontory at Sun Corner (298846), down from the former Rocket Experimental Station. The cliff base, bouldery with narrow segments of shore platform, is difficult of access, but from Sun Corner there is a view of Scratchell's Bay, where the northward-dipping Upper Chalk is crossed by numerous steeply-dipping parallel flint horizons marking the bedding-planes. The beach of sand and flint shingle in this bay consists partly of fresh white-coated and blue-black flints

Above, Fig. 69: Steeply-dipping Upper Chalk with layers of flint along the bedding-planes in the cliff at Watcombe Bay, near Freshwater.

Left, Fig. 70: Goose Rock, the outermost of The Needles, Chalk stacks at the western end of the Isle of Wight. Flint layers mark out the steeply dipping bedding-planes in Upper Chalk hardened by compression resulting from strong earth movements. Note the planed-off foundations of stacks that have disappeared.

eroded from the cliffs and rocky nearshore, and partly of brown flint gravel and sand washed in from the sea floor. Below Sun Corner there are caves and a notch at the base of the cliffs, and an outlying low stack, St. Anthony's Rock, accessible only by boat.

Towards The Needles (Fig. 70) the Upper Chalk becomes very hard and splintery, largely as the result of compression and recrystallisation accompanying the intense folding as the northward dip increases to 75°.

From the Coastguard Cottages there is a view of the three large stacks running out to the red and white lighthouse, persisting because of this hardening. They are shards of Upper Chalk, about 30 metres high, and planed-off intertidal ledges show that there were formerly more of them. A fourth stack, Lot's Wife, was a 35 metre pinnacle that collapsed into the sea in 1764; her stump can still be seen at low tide below the Battery. The innermost stack was joined to the promontory by a natural arch until 1815, when this foundered. In contrast with Whitecliff Point, where similar steeply dipping Upper Chalk reaches the eastern coast of the Isle of Wight, there is no shore platform here, possibly because of greater exposure to south-westerly storm waves.

In the distance the Chalk cliffs of Ballard Down, descending to The Foreland and Old Harry Rocks near Studland, can usually be seen, and it is easy to imagine the Chalk ridge once continuing across the intervening 15 miles (24 km) of open sea.

Alum Bay

The ridge-crest footpath returns from the Battery to Freshwater Bay, but many will want to descend to Alum Bay. This can also be reached by bus from Yarmouth.

North of The Needles the higher horizons in the Upper Chalk are less resistant, and the cliffs facing north across Alum Bay cross successive bedding planes in the steeply dipping rock. From the Battery a road (not available to private cars) and footpath descend the grassy slope above White Cliffs to the car park at Alum Bay. There are good views of the colourful cliffs in steeply dipping Eocene formations in Alum Bay, and the diminishing dip shown by the limestone ledges on the western slopes of Headon Hill.

The Upper Chalk cliffs are best seen from Alum Bay. They have grassy slope segments and buttresses, and a narrow basal ledge. A recent rock fall has produced a white scar, with a large talus apron. At the southern end of Alum Bay the cliffs run in as a wall of chalk beside a deep valley that has been cut into the overlying, almost vertical, Reading Beds (Fig. 71). As in Whitecliff Bay (p. 84) the sub-Palaeocene Chalk surface is rough, furrowed and potholed, and had been planed off almost horizontally in Late Cretaceous and Palaeocene times, before the basal Reading Beds were deposited, and well before the whole sequence was thrown into a nearly vertical structure by Miocene tectonic movements. The coast is exposed to strong wave action generated by westerly storms, and the Lower Tertiary formations have been cut back more quickly north of the fold-hardened Chalk ridge, which thus protrudes further seaward than in Whitecliff Bay. It is worth noting that the steep grassy slope in Upper Chalk above the cliffs has a gradient of 30°-40°, whereas the sub-Palaeocene surface slopes at about 80°, close to the angle of dip (Fig. 71). The grassy slope has therefore been cut back from the plane of the sub-Palaeocene surface, and is not strictly a dip-slope. It is very like the escarpment of Highdown Hill (undercut by sea cliffs) on the other side of the ridge, and as it slopes northward in the same general direction as the dip it may be termed a back-slope[4].

Alum Bay has car parks at the end of B3322, beside the Needles Pleasure Park. A chairlift, as well as a stairway and footpath, descend into an incised valley, and there are steps down to the beach at the mouth of the Alum Bay chine, cut in the Barton Clay, and armoured with boulders. It is best to walk south along the beach (Fig. 18) to the beginning of the Chalk cliff, and work back through the steeply-dipping Lower Tertiary formations from there. As at Whitecliff Bay the cliffs show ribs and ravines cut into vertical layers of variously coloured sand and clay from the red clays of the Palaeocene Reading Beds rapidly up through the Eocene succession northward, the dip diminishing into the Oligocene beds north of the chair lift. There is a small pier, a shingle beach with coarser cobbles towards the southern end, sand with pebble cusps to the north.

The basal Reading Beds in Alum Bay, immediately overlying the eroded Upper Chalk, are coarse, loamy ferruginous sands with flint nodules and pebbles, dipping northward at about 80°. A valley has been cut out in the overlying bright mottled red and purple clays with some white and brown ferruginous clay and occasional pieces of lignite. They are capped northward by the Oldhaven Formation, a 4.3 metre seam of green sandy and shelly silts, and there is then a ridge in sandy clays with flint pebbles and tabular calcareous masses at the base of the London Clay.

The London Clay consists of about 124 metres of almost vertical layers of brown and blue clay and loam bordered northward by equally steep bands of yellow and grey sand interbedded with blue clay and capped by brown and grey laminated clays and sands. The cliffs have been dissected into gulleys along the softer clay seams, between ridges and spurs of sand.

To the north, the cliffs in the Bagshot Sands also show layers of almost vertical strata, with yellow, grey and white sands and thin layers of pipe-clay, followed by variously coloured sands and sandstones (p. 36). A pebble bed marks the beginning of the Bracklesham Beds, which include layers of variously coloured sand, laminated clays, dark organic horizons and some lignite bands, all standing with a high (85°) dip northward. The cliffs are less dissected, but the harder layers form several protruding ribs, including the pebbly horizon beneath the chair lift.

Next comes the valley cut into the dark sandy clays of the overlying Barton Beds. These consist of blue-green, grey and yellow Barton Clay, with some patchy sands and sandy clays and an ironstone band a foot thick near the top. The valley which descends from the Pleasure Park to the shore, beneath the chairlift, is cut in Barton Clay. To the north the Barton Clay is followed by Barton Sand, at first yellow and clayey, then white. The pale yellow and grey Barton Sand north of Alum Bay Chine shows a sudden decline in the northward dip to almost horizontal (Fig. 72). There may be a fault, but it is not clearly exposed.

Alum Bay to Totland Bay

In the northern part of Alum Bay the beach becomes sandy and the cliffs show chutes of slumping clay and lobes of truncated Bracklesham Beds to Hatherwood Point. The Coastal Footpath turns inland over Headon Hill, a heathy upland (also known as Headon Warren because rabbits were farmed here in mediaeval times) with a Plateau Gravel capping (Fig. 11) over Osborne Marls exposed in old gravel pits, and down to Widdick Chine in Totland Bay. The sequence of formations in this part of the Isle of Wight is best described using the most recent subdivisions of the Lower Oligocene Headon and Osborne Beds (Table 4)[2]. The structure of Headon Hill can be explored by walking up to the top of the hill from the western side. There are three cliffs of almost horizontal limestone, separated by heathy slopes on clay or marl, with a basal slumping slope down to the shore (Fig. 72). At the base the Barton Sand is overlain by the marly Totland Bay Beds in a slope that extends up to a 2 metre wall of How Ledge Limestone. Above this another slope in just over 9 metres of muddy Colwell Bay Beds runs up to the prominent cliff of the Hatherwood Limestone, about 8 metres high. Another slope on the Cliff End marls rises to the uppermost cliff of Lacey's Farm Limestone, about 7 metres high, on top of which a gentler slope in overlying Osborne Marls rises to the crest of Headon Hill, capped by Pleistocene sands and gravels.

On the eastern slopes of Headon Hill the Lacey's Farm Limestone forms a structural bench (323861), and there are limestone outcrops at Weston Manor (326866) and above Totland (327870). Trackways on the northern slopes of Headon Hill lead up past a cliffy outcrop of Lacey's Farm Limestone to a slope

Above, Fig. 71: Chalk cliffs on the southern side of Alum Bay, showing the steeply inclined sub-Palaeocene surface, and some of the overlying clays of the Reading Beds in the foreground, with The Needles in the distance. Below, Fig. 72: The transition from the steeply dipping Eocene formations in Alum Bay northward past the Chairlift (on Barton Clay) to the almost horizontal strata of the Headon Beds on Headon Hill.

on the red and grey mottled Osborne Marls, which pass upward to the prominent white Bembridge Limestone cliff outcropping near the top of the hill. The heathy slopes are convex above the Bembridge Limestone, and concave with landslides below.

It is possible at low tide to walk and scramble from Hatherfield Point to Totland along a shore which is strewn with large and small fallen limestone boulders over clay, derived from cliffed strata high on the slopes of Headon Warren, a slumping scrubby slope. The cliffs decline into low bluffs with boulders and subsided edges, outcrops of clay and a protruding reef of limestone as the coast swings eastward. There are sectors of narrow sand and gravel beach, with flint and limestone pebbles, and blocks of pale sandstone and limestone that have slumped down on to the shore. These are draped with black wrack (Fucus) or bright green weed (Verrucaria), and between them are soft muddy patches. The shingle beach fades eastward into lobes of clay, some of which have buried fallen trees. There is a fringe of green weedy limestone boulders over clay, then brown sand that has been washed in from the sea floor. The slumping lobes have been cliffed by marine erosion, and as the clay is washed out pebbles, cobbles, boulders and blocks are left littering the shore. Away to the north Albert Fort juts out at Cliff End, then Hurst Castle on a shingle spit across the strait.

The slumping bluffs come to an end on the southern side of Totland Bay, and there is a sector of low cliff in stratified clayey sands. From Widdick Chine the Coastal Footpath runs along the promenade behind a sea wall, with groynes and shingle beaches and a sandy foreshore exposed at low tide to a little pier. The sea defences at Totland Bay were built in 1966, but clay from the backing bluff still slumps down over the back wall on to the promenade in wet weather. The bluffs north of Totland Pier look more stable, but there is occasional slumping, with flint gravel in the sliding clay.

Totland Bay is crossed by a small anticline, over which the Headon and Osborne Beds rise in a gentle arch along the coasts of Totland Bay and Colwell Bay. They include blue and green clays alternating with sands, sandy limestones and shelly limestones. The slumping bluffs behind the Totland Bay promenade are in the pale sandy and silty marls of the Totland Bay Beds, within which a soft limestone develops at Warden Point. This has been indurated where the outcrop runs down across the shore to form Warden Ledge.

Colwell Bay

At Warden Point the promenade curves round into Colwell Bay, and ends past Colwell Chine above How Ledge, another limestone running out across the shore. This is the pale brown How Ledge Limestone above the Totland Bay Beds, a layer that has descended from the northern slopes of Headon Hill. The walk continues along the shingle beach round the bay below slumping bluffs which steepen into cliffs in the Colwell Bay beds, grey marls overlain by light brown and yellow beds that dip northward, passing across Brambles Chine.

The Coastal Footpath turns inland at Brambles Chine to climb the hill to the wooded crest of West Cliff and descend to the shore at Fort Victoria. It is possible to walk along the shore to the north end of Colwell Bay, but there are difficulties in crossing private land beyond this.

The muddy shore just north of How Ledge is cut across the Colwell Bay Beds, which include a basal Neritina Bed, with shell beds in sand and clay, capped by the Venus Bed, with oysters in blue, green and brown sandy clay seen in the base of the cliff and on either side of Brambles Chine. The upper part of the cliff is cut in silts and sands of the Linstone Chine beds, which decline northward to Linstone Chine, and are thrown upward by a transverse anticlinal flexure that raises the Colwell Bay beds in the cliff outcrop, then brings them back down to pass below sea level. Cliff-top gravels on either side of Linstone Chine indicate that it was incised into an earlier broad and gentle valley.

There used to be sandy shoals visible at low tide in Colwell Bay, but they were removed by dredging, and as a result stronger waves have accelerated erosion during storms. The beach consists of angular and subrounded flint gravel, with some limestone pebbles. The cliffs have receded north of a groyne that retains protective shingle. Beyond Linstone Chine the cliffs become irregular, and there is an outcrop of about a metre of pale Hatherwood Limestone above a slumping promontory with a ruined sea wall and blockhouses.

The overlying Osborne Beds descend to the coast towards Cliff End, where the outcrop is much broken by slumping. Fort Albert projects boldly at Cliff End, and as the shore is impassable it is necessary to walk back to Brambles Chine and resume the Coastal Footpath.

Fort Albert to Yarmouth

The coast north-east from Fort Albert is best seen by walking westward along the shore from Sconce Point at Fort Victoria. The broad scrubby bluffs and unstable sloping cliffs are cut in Osborne Marls, with lobes down to a shore where soft clay is littered with boulders from the overlying Bembridge Limestone. Lumps of limestone have accumulated on the shore near Round Tower Point, where they are encrusted with dark seaweed. In this part of the Isle of Wight the Bembridge Limestone is about 5 metres thick, but it does not form shore ledges of the kind seen on the eastern coast. It is capped by Bembridge Marls on the wooded ridge that runs north-eastward, parallel to the coastline.

A sea wall protects Fort Victoria, round Sconce Point, then a beach terrace of brown shingle runs below a wooded bluff. The sea wall resumes to the east, towards Yarmouth. There are some groynes, a protruding stone structure, weedy boulders and a brown shingle beach with concrete walling at the top, backed by the Western Yar estuary, and ending in the breakwater that protects Yarmouth harbour.

The Western Yar incised a deep valley here during low sea level phases of the Pleistocene, then Late Quaternary marine submergence produced a typical drowned valley system, which has become an estuary bordered by tidal mudflats and salt marshes with areas of Spartina grass, threaded by tidal creeks. The Spartina was introduced here nearly a century ago[72], and at first built up bordering muddy terraces, but now it is eroding along the seaward edges. The Coastal Footpath detours inland across a low terrace of the Western Yar (p. 58), then round the estuary, crossing a bridge at Norton (348872), and returning by way of the abandoned railway that ran from Freshwater to Yarmouth.

East of the estuary, Yarmouth has a Castle and a wooden pier, and a sea wall along the waterfront, past the Royal Solent Yacht Club and houses built to the water's edge. There are minor beaches with brown shingle, and at low tide a spread of mainly flint gravel is exposed.

Yarmouth to Newtown Bay

The Osborne Beds pass below sea level near Yarmouth, together with the Bembridge Limestone, so that the bluffs east of Yarmouth are cut in Bembridge Marls. To the east a sea wall fronts grassy lawns, and groynes divide a gravelly beach behind a muddy shore that is submerged at high tide. The Coastal Footpath runs along the sea wall and up to the car park at Viewpoint Bouldnor. It then follows the A3054 east from Bouldnor until a track to the left down a signposted gravel lane leads into Bouldnor Forest. The coast here consists of low receding cliffs in grey clay, a narrow gravel beach, undercut slopes, and fallen trees. The Bembridge Marls disappear beneath the Hamstead Beds and pass below sea level, so that when the slumping cliffs begin they are entirely in the Hamstead Beds.

These are coloured clays, loams, sands and shales, dipping north-eastward. A little valley opens to a shingle beach backed by reedswamp, with a clifflet in swamp clays. On the coast between Bouldnor and Hamstead Ledge the Bouldnor Formation consists of about 18 metres of green, blue and black clays and marls (weathering to brown), white bands, and carbonaceous layers. The upper part (Cranmore Beds) is of marine origin, the youngest of the Oligocene formations seen on the Isle of Wight. The coastal bluffs are slumping (Fig. 73), and as the ground behind the slopes landward they are diminishing in height.

Fig. 73: Slumping Hamstead Beds in Bouldnor Cliff.

The Coastal Footpath climbs behind Bouldnor Cliff, north of Cranmore, where the Hamstead Beds are capped by flinty Plateau Gravel, and form a seaward slope that is unstable, especially in wet weather. There are ledges, mud-streams and mud-falls, and the drying mud has cracks or crevasses, like a glacier[53]. The crumbling and slumping clay cliffs continue east along the edge of pine plantations. There are outlying ruins of an old pier. The cliff crest is scalloped, a breakaway above the landslides, some of which are bare, some scrubby. The path climbs as the breakaway recedes, with clay cliffs above scrub woodland. Angular gravels and occasional rounded pebbles in a brown clay matrix form a vertical wall up to a metre high at the top of these cliffs. There have been some inland diversions of the coastal footpath because of landslides in the Oligocene clays.

The Coastal Footpath leaves the plantations and crosses meadows, passing farms and houses, with views southward over a wide lowland to the central Chalk ridge. The footpath comes out on to lanes, leading to Cranmore Avenue, which becomes Seaview Road. Past West Hamstead Farm another footpath runs down through the woods, descending to a muddy eroding scrubby shore, where at high tide waves lap at the clay edge. There are sectors of basal cliff in white shelly debris with interbedded grey-green clays.

To the east a landslide lobe projects into the sea, truncated by wave attack, and there is a scar on the backing slope. Hamstead Cliff, to the east, has slumping breakaways, and the Coastal Footpath follows the declining cliff crest. The cliff top at Cranmore has receded at up to 3 metres per year[73]. There are landslides in the Osborne Beds over the Bembridge Marls, which reappear and rise along the base of the cliffs to form the bluff that curves inland west of the Newtown River valley. As it does so, basal ledges of Bembridge Limestone, three stone beds with intervening softer bands, run out westward across the shore and into the sea as Hamstead Ledge. A storm-piled beach of brown subangular flint shingle, capped by minor dunes, continues as the cliffs come to an end, becoming a spit that curves back into the entrance to Newtown Harbour.

The Coastal Footpath here turns inland. Alternatively, one can walk back through lanes and footpaths to Bouldnor Copse and Yarmouth.

Newtown Harbour

Behind the spit, Newtown Harbour is a branching drowned valley system, an estuary much used by yachts and motor boats. Like the Yarmouth estuary, it is the product of Late Quaternary marine submergence, followed by formation of paired spits bordering the marine entrance, the accumulation of muddy sediment and the spreading of salt marshes, including Spartina introduced about a century ago. There are breached segments of an older recurved spit inside the western entrance. Streams from small incised valleys flow into the converging tidal channels, which are bordered by mudflats and salt marshes. The bordering slopes decline gently to the salt marshes, without any cliffs or bluffs.

There have been attempts to enclose and reclaim parts of the Newtown Harbour salt marshes, notably in the 17th century, to form pastureland. The largest of these was abandoned after the sea flooded them in a 1954 storm. The remains of the enclosing wall persist between Newtown River and Clamerkin Lake, north of the village of Newtown, and it is possible to walk out along the western wall for views of the lower part of Newtown Harbour and the marine entrance, bordered by spits.

Newtown Bay to Cowes

West of Newtown Harbour the Coastal Footpath turns inland behind scrub. It crosses creeks and inlets with salt marsh on the western shores of Newtown Harbour, and runs across subdued meadowland interfluves. It continues south on to the Hamstead Beds, skirting a promontory with a jetty and boat park, turns up into woodlands to Pigeon Coo Farm (401902), then south to the A3054 and east to Shalfleet.

The coast east of Newtown Harbour is inaccessible because of military restrictions. From the coast to the west it can be seen that the shingle spit, capped by sand dunes, becomes a beach eastward in front of scrubby bluffs 10 to 15 metres high, with two sectors of clay cliff. These cliffs are cut in Bembridge Marls, overlying Bembridge Limestone and Osborne Marls. Patches of Bembridge Limestone outcrop on the shore.

The Coastal Footpath from Shalfleet follows lanes to Newtown and Locksgreen, eventually reaching the coast through the Thorness Holiday Centre and caravan park, down across fields to Thorness Bay. Alternatively, it is possible to reach Thorness Bay by walking westward along the Coastal Footpath from Cowes.

North of the Thorness Holiday Centre, in Burnt Wood, a footpath descends to the coast, which consists of wooded slumping brown bluffs up to 40 metres high in Bembridge Marls, with a basal cliff a few centimetres high and wave-cut ramps in clay. Undermined trees have collapsed on to the shore. Bembridge Limestone outcrops locally at the base of the cliff and forms a shore platform, Saltmead Ledge, made slippery by mud and seaweed, with broken edges facing seaward.

The cliffs decline eastward into Thorness Bay, where the wide muddy foreshore exposed at low tide has ledges of Bembridge Limestone, and is backed by sandy beach ridges on a spit that deflects the little stream eastward. The Coastal Footpath crosses this stream by way of a small bridge, and climbs along the edge of slumping scrubby terraced bluffs that rise to the east, across a truncated upland. The Bembridge Limestone forms reefs running out across the shore, notably at Gurnard Ledge, while the bluffs consist of slumping Bembridge Marls, overlain by Hamstead Beds.

Beyond Gurnard Ledge the cliffs become vegetated bluffs, with a basal bench of Bembridge Limestone continuing eastward to the mouth of Gurnard Luck. There has been some slumping in the overlying in Bembridge Marls, especially in and after wet weather. The Coastal Footpath follows the top of the bluffs and descends to the mouth of the Gurnard Luck valley, where there is a bridge over a small stream.

Beyond this valley the vegetated coastal bluffs rise again behind Gurnard Bay. The Coastal Footpath runs inland, but there is access to the shore from Solent View Road, down Worsley Road to the lookout over Gurnard Bay. The coastal slope is now a degraded escarpment, with hummocky slopes on the Bembridge Marls dipping southward, and patchy outcrops of Bembridge Limestone along the shore. The Esplanade, with a sea wall and a narrow beach of flint gravel, curves past Egypt Point round to the Royal Yacht Squadron at Cowes Castle.

Cowes, beside the Medina estuary, is built on a gravel-capped hill where slopes in Bembridge Marls descend to Bembridge Limestone on the shore. Plateau Gravel caps the Cowes spur, and is draped some distance down the coastal slope. The lower slopes on either side of the Medina estuary are cut into the Osborne Beds, the Bembridge Limestone descending southward to pass beneath the estuary near the sewage works.

Cowes to Ryde

The Medina estuary lies in another drowned valley, but one which runs almost straight, with only minor tributaries north of Newtown. It opens northward past Cowes to the Solent. The coast east of the estuary, through to Wootton Creek and on to Ryde is difficult of access from the land because of private ownership. The so-called Coastal Path makes another lengthy detour inland, from East Cowes along the A3201 and Alverston Road to Wootton Bridge, and then by way of Fishbourne and Quarr Road, across a golf course (Ladies' Walk) and down into Ryde. The intervening coast can be seen from the sea, and it is possible to land on some parts of the shore at low tide.

In fact this part of the coast is not particularly interesting. East from the breakwater at East Cowes the coast road soon comes to an end at Old Castle Point, but at low tide it is possible to walk out across the shore and see that the coast of Osborne Bay consists mainly of steep wooded bluffs with only minor basal cliffing, and narrow beaches of sand and shingle behind a shore that is muddy at low tide. The basal cliffs are cut into the Osborne Beds, which are here red and green clays with occasional bands of shelly limestone. The former cliffs at Osborne have been graded and planted with vegetation.

Fig. 74: Wootton Creek, one of the estuarine inlets on the north coast of the Isle of Wight, with an entrance partly blocked by a shingle spit.

The bluffs are interrupted by a tidal creek at the mouth of steep-sided valley of Palmer's Creek, which is constricted by spits of sand and shingle at King's Quay. A cliff is cut into the Bembridge Limestone, underlain by red, green and blue clays and shales of the Osborne Beds, and slopes rise inland on the Bembridge Marls, the higher spurs capped with Plateau Gravel.

On the coastal bluffs there have been small landslides, notably to the east of Old Castle Point, below Norris Castle, and there has been cliff recession west of Wootton Creek, where the shore has been armoured with boulders and concrete. There are beaches of brown subangular flint shingle, derived from Plateau Gravel deposits capping the coastal bluffs. The estuary of Wootton Creek, yet another drowned valley system, is tidal below Wootton Bridge, and shrinks to a narrow channel between mudflats at low tide. A road north from the traffic lights on the A3054 leads to the car ferry terminal at Fishbourne, and at the mouth of the estuary there are bordering shingle beaches and spits (Fig. 74). Wooded bluffs resume to the east, where the Bembridge Limestone outcrops patchily on the shore below Quarr Abbey. The low cliffs at Binstead are cut into the Osborne Beds, red and green marls capped by a shelly bed, then sandstones and grits.

A sea wall begins at Pelhamfield, behind a wide sandy shore with some gravel exposed at low tide, and steps lead up on to the esplanade by the Prince Consort building at the western end of Ryde. The traverse round the island is completed on reaching the pier at Ryde.

INLAND EXCURSIONS

Introduction

Having explored the coastline, the landscape of the Isle of Wight can be examined in relation to geological outcrops on a series of twelve inland excursions. The first two cross the island from north to south and back, traversing the outcrops of all the geological formations with the exception of the basal Wealden Beds. These are followed by excursions from east to west along the Central Downs, with an intervening walk on St. George's Down, south-east of Newport. Two short walks from Godshill illustrate features of the lowland south of the Central Downs, and then the Southern Plateau is explored on foot, followed by a short excursion above St. Lawrence. The formations in the southern half of the island are traversed in a walk from Niton to Newport, and details of the escarpments to the west and the Weald Clay lowland down to the coast are seen on a circular walk from Mottistone Down. Finally, Bembridge Limestone features in the north-west are explored in the country around Newbridge.

Hazards

The suggested itineraries for inland field excursions on the Isle of Wight follow public roads and footpaths. While traffic is generally much less dense than on the mainland, it is still necessary to be careful, particularly on the smaller lanes, some of which may be used by local drivers not expecting to encounter on-coming cars. One should stop and get out of the car to look at geological outcrops and landform features, or to enjoy a viewpoint, and be prepared to walk along footpaths to get to the points of interest.

Apart from a few natural exposures (such as the Upper Greensand chert beds in inland cliffs) most geological formations are seen in roadside cuttings or in active or disused quarries. Access to quarries requires prior permission, and when examining geological features in quarries one should beware of the risk of falling rocks or sudden slumping.

These various hazards should not deter people from exploring the Isle of Wight, but due care should be taken (see Notice on page 11).

Excursion 1

A North-South Road Traverse: Wootton to Blackgang

This excursion (Fig. 75) begins at Wootton Bridge (547919), about 5 km west of Ryde on the A3054 road to Newport. The country north of the Central Downs has an undulating topography on the Oligocene Hamstead Beds, where valleys cut by north-flowing streams alternate with gravel-strewn interfluvial ridges. It is evident that a formerly extensive plateau has been dissected by the incision and widening of the river valleys.

West from Wootton Bridge the A3054 climbs across a north-south ridge, the crest of which is just over 50 metres above sea level. There is a capping of Plateau Gravel (p. 42), mainly flint pebbles in an earthy matrix, one of several such hill cappings at about this level in the northern part of the island. At Wootton the A3055 (signposted Sandown) runs along a rising interfluve on the Hamstead Beds to Knight's Cross, and on up to the Central Downs Chalk ridge above Downend. South from Knight's Cross Plateau Gravel caps this ridge, rising to more than 80 metres above sea level towards the Chalk, which was the source of the flint pebbles (Fig. 10). They were carried northward across a broad gentle slope by streams fed by melting snow for a distance of up to 5 miles (8 km) over a surface now between 50 and 80 metres above present sea level which has since been much dissected by river valleys.

From the Hare and Hounds Inn, Downend Road runs southward, down the Chalk escarpment and a spur of Upper Greensand, across narrow outcrops of Gault, Carstone and the Sandrock Beds, past Arreton Manor, and on to the Ferruginous Sands. At Arreton Cross Plateau Gravel, mainly flint pebbles, extends along sandstone spurs on either side of a valley that becomes incised south-eastward from the A3056. This road swings right at Crouchers Cross, and Merstone Lane runs off southward across a gentle declining slope on the sandstones, which end in a scarp overlooking the Eastern Yar valley. This Lane is followed through Merstone, close to the divide between the Yar and the Blackwater tributary of the Medina River, which has here been beheaded by river capture (p. 55). The road then crosses a small tributary of the Eastern Yar, and swings west to Bohemia Corner, below a spur of the Sandrock scarp, to join the A3020.

A little to the south Chequers Inn Road (to the right) climbs a spur of the Sandrock scarp, which has a capping of flint gravel. A fork to the right comes to a north-south road beside the Chequers Inn (511830), and this climbs southward along the western side of Bleak Down (512815), a gravel-capped ridge of sandstone in the upper Ferruginous Sands, on a slope that descends into the

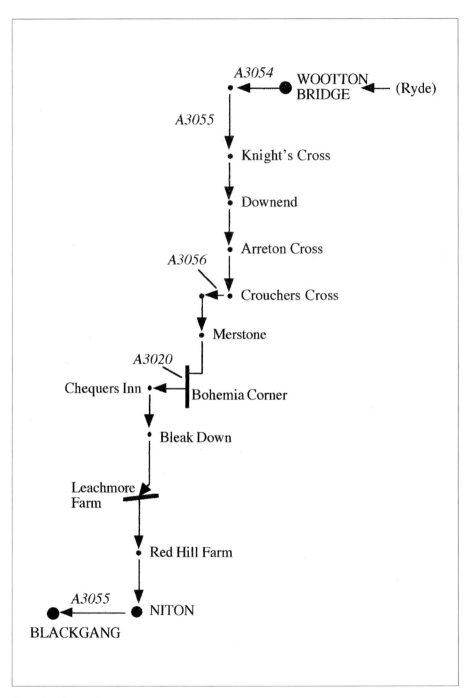

Fig. 75: Excursion 1

Medina valley. Past Leachmore Farm a left turn (508807) towards Niton ascends to the sloping Sandrock Beds near Fairfields (609798), then the Carstone scarp at Red Hill Farm (512788), and along the valley in the Gault, with some hummocky landslide topography, through Kingates. The valley narrows towards the Niton Gap, between steepening Upper Greensand, the Chert Beds forming a bench on either side, and above these is the Lower Chalk of St. Catherine's Hill to the west. At Niton turn right along the A3055, up a dry valley bordered by steep slopes in the Chert Beds, over the Chalk spur and down to the car park at Blackgang. Various walks can be made from here to see the coast (p. 102), or to explore St. Catherine's Down (page 159).

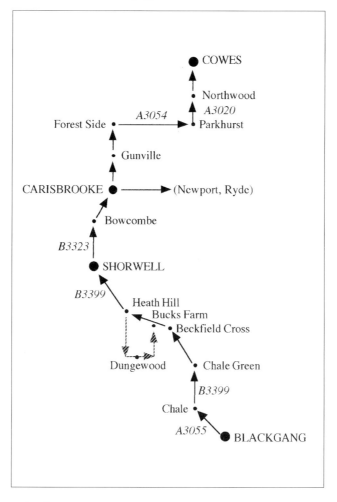

Fig. 76: Excursion 2.

Excursion 2

A South-North Road Traverse: Blackgang to Cowes

This excursion (Fig. 76) returns northward across the island. From Blackgang the Military Road (A3055) descends a slope where former landslides of Chalk and Upper Greensand mantle the Gault outcrop, to the bench on the Sandrock Beds at Chale. At the church turn right on to the B3399 northward through Chale, edging off the Sandrock Beds on to the Ferruginous Sands. Towards Chale Green the Medina River rises, and is soon incised into a valley running to the north-east. Town Lane (B3399) swings westward, away from this valley, up a dip slope of sandstone in the upper part of the Ferruginous Sands (Sands of Walpen Undercliff) then northward along a ridge just behind a west-facing escarpment cut in this sandstone, to Beckfield Cross (482810). At Kingston the sandstone escarpment is breached by a valley cut by a headstream of Atherfield Brook, but it can be seen again to the west, on Gun Hill (471812). At its base is a seepage zone along the outcrop of the underlying Foliated Sand and Clay, the scarp having been cut back as a result of spring sapping[74].

B3399 continues north-west, in front of dissected spurs of the south-facing scarp of the Sandrock Beds, to Heath Hill. From here is a view southward past Dungewood to Warren Hill, along a small west-facing escarpment developed on a sandstone at a lower level in the Ferruginous Sands, possibly the Walpen and Ladder Sand (Table 3).

A detour may be made on footpaths to the south to explore this escarpment. These lead to Dungewood Lane (460811), which climbs from Atherfield Brook to ascend this escarpment near Warren Hill, where it is a steep feature, then turn north in front of the higher Gun Hill (Sands of Walpen Undercliff) escarpment to Bucks Farm, and so back to the B3399.

From Heath Hill B3399 crosses the Sandrock Beds outcrop at Sandy Way. To the north, beyond a Gault vale, is the bolder parallel escarpment of the cherty Upper Greensand, through which a river gap has been cut at Shorwell. B3323 runs northward through the village and up Shorwell Shute, the valley cut into the Chalk. The road crosses a col (106 metres) to descend the dry Cheverton valley, curving north-eastward and cut in Lower and Middle Chalk. There are smooth, rounded slopes characteristic of Chalk country, with coombes opening down to Bowcombe, where Lukely Brook rises. The northern side of the valley becomes steeper on the Upper Chalk along Bowcombe Down, and B3323 continues through the gap cut by Lukely Brook to Carisbrooke, the castle standing on a hill of Upper Chalk to the east.

At Carisbrooke a lane runs northward through Gunville, crossing outcrops of Reading Beds, London Clay and Bagshot Beds in a gentle valley followed by a low ridge on the Headon and Bembridge Beds, then a wide gently undulating area on the Hamstead Beds to Forest Side (478897). Forest Road (A3054) to the right meets the A3020 that runs northward through Parkhurst on the Hamstead Beds. The ridge rises towards Northwood, where it is capped by Plateau Gravel, and then descends into Cowes over a gentle slope of Bembridge Marls, at the base of which Bembridge Limestone outcrops patchily along the shore.

Excursion 3

Central Downs between Brading and Newport

This excursion (Fig. 77) begins at Brading, where the Chalk ridge of the Central Downs is breached by a gap cut by the Eastern Yar, on its way down to Bembridge Harbour. From Yarbridge a road runs up on to Brading Down, where the car park provides a good viewpoint. To the south-east is the Boating Lake at Sandown, then the Lower Greensand ridge at Yaverland and the higher Chalk escarpment of Bembridge Down, with its Monument and Fort. Southward the Chalk escarpment descends steeply, and is fronted by a hogsbacked ridge of Upper Greensand with a scarp facing south across the lowland excavated in the Sandown Anticline. Beyond the low-lying area on the Wealden Beds behind Sandown the ground rises to the Ferruginous Sands of Shanklin, with Knock Cliff showing these capped by the Sandrock Beds. Behind and to the west are the Upper Greensand and Lower Chalk escarpments rising to the Southern Plateau, and forming three spurs (St. Martin's Down, Appuldurcombe Down and St. Catherine's Down) with intervening valleys.

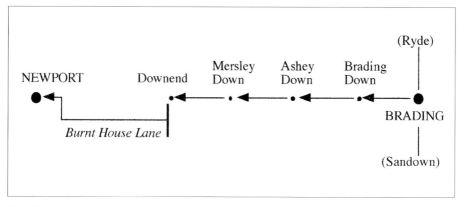

Fig. 77: Excursion 3.

Westward is an extensive undulating lowland on the Ferruginous Sands, drained by the Eastern Yar and its tributaries, and rising to Bleak Down on the ridge south of Rookley, which is the watershed between the Eastern Yar and the Medina River. The north-facing Upper Greensand and Chalk escarpments are matched across the area between the Sandown and Brighstone Anticlines (Fig. 2) by south-facing escarpments of these formations at Berry Hill and Chillerton Down, with its tall television mast.

To the north of the road on Brading Down a footpath leads down the Chalk dip-slope, and there are views across to the Ryde plateau, Spithead and Portsmouth, the ridge of Ports Down with its prominent Chalk quarry, then eastward to St. Helens, Bembridge Harbour and the Bembridge Plateau; beyond that Selsey Bill, the South Downs dip slope running away to the east.

The road runs westward along the Central Downs, and there are similar views from Ashey Down (575875) and Mersley Down (558874) (Fig. 78). Below the Chalk escarpment a valley has been cut out in the Lower Chalk, and the Upper Greensand ridge is prominent east and west of Knighton, with a bench capped by the Carstone to the south. The road continues westward along the Chalk ridge to the Hare and Hounds Inn at Downend, beyond which Burnt House Lane edges along the steep Upper Chalk dip-slope and bordering Reading Beds, down into Newport.

Fig. 78: The view from Mersley Down, on the central Chalk ridge southward across the vale cut into the Sandown Anticline to the Chalk-capped Southern Plateau.

Excursion 4

A Walk on St. George's Down

South of Newport (Fig. 79) St. George's Lane climbs the Chalk escarpment on the eastern side of the Medina valley to a plateau between 90 and 100 metres above sea level, which has been cut across the Upper Greensand, Gault, Carstone and Sandrock formations, and ends in a south-facing escarpment on Ferruginous Sands. This is St. George's Down, which has the appearance of a remnant of a once extensive plateau, on which the topography shows no contrasts between geological formations that elsewhere have been strongly differentiated by dissection and erosion. St. George's Down is capped by Plateau Gravel, consisting of angular flints and cherts derived from the Chalk and Greensands. The surface has been modified by the excavation of sand and gravel from pits on the plateau, and quarries in the southern escarpment of Ferruginous Sands.

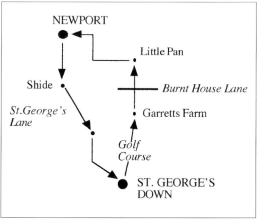

Fig. 79: Excursion 4.

From the western edge of the St. George's Down plateau there are views across the Medina valley to the Upper Greensand bench above Whitcombe Manor and, beyond that, the Chalk escarpment rising to Bowcombe Down. In front of Whitcombe Manor the pinewoods of Marvel Copse pick out a ridge of Carstone. To the south is the Rookley ridge, bordered by steep slopes in the Sandrock Beds, capped by hard Carstone and some Gault, and surmounted by a small east-west ridge at Gossard Hill (504841), an outlier of Upper Greensand capped by resistant chert beds, west of Rookley village. This country can be explored by following the A3020 south to Rookley and taking a footpath that runs west from the village and round the surmounting ridge.

To the south-east of St. George's Down is a broad undulating lowland on the lower divisions of the Ferruginous Sands, dissected by the Eastern Yar and its tributaries, with an extensive river terrace, notably on Hole Common. Beyond Godshill is the Sandrock bench, the scarp rising to the Upper Greensand chert beds, and the promontories of Chalk escarpment bordering the Southern Plateau.

A footpath crosses the Golf Course and descends to Garrett's Farm (513873), and on down the northern slopes of St. George's Down. There are several small coombes cut by streams rising at the base of the gravels. The Chalk dip-slope drops steeply into the Pan valley, which has been cut out along the outcrop of the Bagshot Beds. The streams disappear underground into swallow-holes on the Upper Chalk, and there are seepages along the junction with the Reading Beds down the slope.

The footpath continues across Burnt House Lane, down to the stream near Little Pan (515884), beyond which the ground rises on the Bembridge Marls and Hamstead Beds to Staplers Hill (89 metres), capped by another patch of Plateau Gravel, similar to those on St. George's Hill and on the spur below Downend, to the east. The landscape is the outcome of dissection of a once extensive plateau by right-bank tributaries of the Medina River, leaving St. George's Down as a residual upland.

From Little Pan the footpath turns left along the valley side, down to join Pan Lane, which runs back into Newport.

Excursion 5

Central Downs between Newport and Freshwater

This excursion (Fig. 80) continues the westward traverse made in Excursion 3 along the Central Downs. From Carisbrooke, west of Newport, Tennyson Trail climbs the Chalk ridge on Bowcombe Down, which is capped by a spread of angular flint gravel. The Central Downs are narrow east of Newport and west of Brighstone Down where the Chalk dips northward at between 60° and 85°, but they widen in the intervening area where the dip diminishes between the Sandown and Brighstone Anticlines (Fig. 2). South and south-west from Bowcombe Down the Chalk forms a wide plateau dissected by deep, now dry, valleys cut by headwaters of streams flowing north and south, as well as tributaries of the Medina River, as above Gatcombe (Fig. 9).

Tennyson Trail runs south-westward across this high country. To the north the Upper Chalk slope descends to the Tertiary edge, with woodlands on the Reading Beds along the B4301 between Apesdown and Ashengrove.

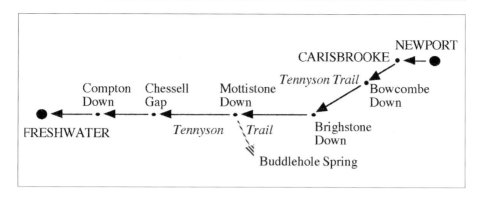

Fig. 80: Excursion 5.

Tennyson Trail continues through Brighstone Forest, out on to the crest of the Chalk escarpment overlooking Brighstone. Here the view southward is over a narrow Upper Greensand bench to the Gault vale which rises westward in front of Mottistone Down (Fig. 81). Beyond this vale is a ridge consisting of Carstone, Sandrock Beds and Ferruginous Sands, the latter forming a south-facing scarp which is breached by a transverse valley at Brighstone. Then the

Fig. 81: The Chalk escarpment at Mottistone Down, with the Gault vale in the foreground.

151

ground declines to a gently undulating lowland on the generally soft Wealden Beds, truncated by the receding cliffs along the coast between Atherfield Point and Compton Bay. West from Brighstone Down Tennyson Trail follows the crest of the Chalk escarpment to the col (421845) at the head of the Calbourne valley, where Lynch Lane, between Calbourne and Brighstone, crosses the Central Downs. There is a car park here, a starting point for the walk from Mottistone Down south to the coast (Excursion 11). Lynch Lane descends the Chalk and Upper Greensand escarpment diagonally, and at the base (the junction with the Gault clay) Buddlehole Spring (423843) flows out into a small coombe.

Tennyson Trail runs on along Mottistone Down to the Chessell Gap, where the Central Downs are crossed by a valley at the head of Caul Bourne, and then along Wellow Down to Compton Down. The south-facing Chalk escarpment is fronted by sectors of valley cut out along the Gault, then by the Lower Greensand ridge, with the Ferruginous Beds forming another south-facing escarpment, somewhat dissected by steep coombes at the heads of small streams flowing down across the lowlands on the Wealden Beds, as at Brook Hill. From the crest of Compton Down, above the Chalk cliffs of Compton Bay, the view south-eastward is across the Compton Farm valley, cut out along the Gault outcrop, and the Lower Greensand ridge to the cliffs cut in the Wealden Beds between Hanover Point and Atherfield Point. In the distance are sandstone ridges, and the Upper Greensand and Chalk escarpments rising above Blackgang.

Excursion 6

A Walk from Godshill to Bleak Down

The extensive outcrop of Ferruginous Sands west of Shanklin forms undulating country, dissected by headstreams of the Eastern Yar. Typical features may be seen in the course of a short walk (Fig. 82) from Godshill, which stands on a spur of sandstone within the upper part of the Ferruginous Sands, probably equivalent to the Sands of Walpen Undercliff (p. 29), with basal seepage at the junction with the underlying Foliated Clay and Sand, as on the South Down-Kingston ridge. From the car park east of the village (530816) Hollies Lane runs south-west, and becomes a sunken lane bordered by this sandstone, climbing to cross Sheepwash Lane. It continues south-west, down a little valley to the Whitwell Road. A little to the right is Beacon Alley, a left turning that descends to a gravelly terrace about 40 metres above sea level, a former valley floor of the Eastern Yar.

The river is now incised into it to a depth of about 7 metres below the terrace, which is also seen on the western side at Lavender's Farm. Beacon Alley climbs through a sunken lane where the Godshill sandstone is again exposed, and a footpath leads up on to Bleak Down, a north-south ridge of this sandstone capped by flint and chert pebble gravels 70-80 metres above sea level. These are typical of river terrace gravels, on remnants of a former valley floor of the Medina River, now dissected by the Medina and adjacent headstreams of the Eastern Yar. The river gravels decline northward to about 60 metres near Blackwater, where the former valley floor narrowed to pass through a gap in the Central Downs.

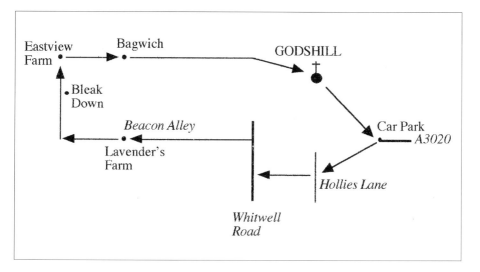

Fig. 82: Excursion 6.

At the northern end of Bleak Down near Eastview Farm (512821) a footpath descends eastward, through Bagwich and back across the Eastern Yar valley with its bordering river terraces, back into Godshill.

Excursion 7

A Walk from Godshill to Gat Cliff

From Godshill there is a view southward to the Sandrock Beds escarpment, which rises behind Sainham Farm (528810), then the Upper Greensand escarpment with cherty sandstone outcrops on Gat Cliff, surmounted by the Chalk escarpment. These features can be explored (Fig. 83) by going south along Sheepwash Lane and (526808) taking a footpath to the left, past Sainham Farm. This ascends the Sandrock Beds on an escarpment (530808) capped by hard Carstone, crosses a slight valley, then climbs through hummocky terrain on former landslides where the Upper Greensand disintegrated and subsided over the Gault Clay. The ground becomes sandy at the base of Gat Cliff (534805), a steep escarpment in Upper Greensand with layered chert beds outcropping in cliffy segments near the top (Fig. 84). Above this is the Chalk escarpment rising to Appuldurcombe Down.

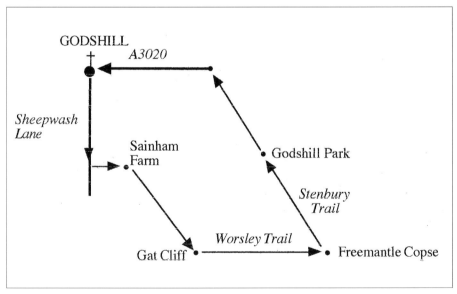

Fig. 83: Excursion 7.

Worsley Trail runs eastward below Gat Cliff to Freemantle Copse, where Stenbury Trail leads north-westward across the Carstone and Sandrock bench, here partly mantled with slumped Gault clay, to Godshill Park. Then comes a descent, beside a small valley cut into the sandstones of the upper Ferruginous Sands, to the Shanklin Road (A3029) and back into Godshill.

Fig. 84: Gat Cliff, a north-facing escarpment in the Chert Beds (Upper Greensand). The field in the foreground is on the underlying Gault clay.

Excursion 8

A Walk on the Southern Plateau

The best way of understanding the geology and topography of the Southern Plateau is by walking across it (Fig. 85). A traverse can be made from Ventnor, up through the Zigzag to a track that climbs the Upper Greensand to the brow of Lower Chalk at Rew Down. A footpath crosses the golf course to join the Stenbury Trail, which comes up the eastern side of a coombe past the sports ground, and runs between fences beside the golf course. The land rises gradually northward on the Lower Chalk from Week Down across Stenbury Down to Appuldurcombe Down. On either side there are views of similar gradual ascents, on the eastern side, across the deep Wroxall valley cut by an Eastern Yar headstream, the rise is from Luccombe Down to St. Martin's Down, while to the west, across the wider Whitwell valley, cut by the upper Eastern Yar, there is a similar rise on St. Catherine's Down.

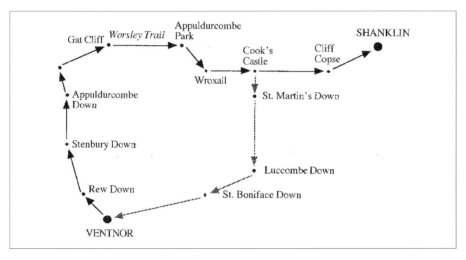

Fig. 85: Excursion 8.

Stenbury Trail climbs towards the radio station on the summit of Appuldurcombe Down, and the views open out in all directions. Westward is the broad lowland beyond Chale, the Chalk escarpment running away from the tall mast on Chillerton Down until it is undercut by the white cliffs of Compton Bay and Highdown Hill, beyond Freshwater. On a clear day the Bournemouth cliffs, the lowlands of Poole Harbour, and the ridges of Ballard Down and Durlston Head on either side of Swanage Bay can be seen in the distance. To the north is the Medina Gap at Newport, flanked by the Upper Greensand at Gatcombe on one side and the St. George's Down plateau on the other. Eastward across the lowland behind Shanklin and Sandown is the Chalk of Culver Cliff. A footpath (signposted Godshill) skirts the fenced enclosure of the radio station, and descends beside a coombe in the Chalk escarpment. In front of this escarpment is a prominent bench in the Upper Greensand, ending in the steep slope of Gat Cliff, below which are hummocky landslides over the Gault. Ahead are the ridges and valleys around Godshill, the south-facing Greensand and Chalk escarpments above Arreton, and the incised valley of the Medina River, heading for the Newport Gap. To the west is a similar Upper Greensand bench running north from St. Catherine's Hill to end in a steep wooded drop below Hoy's Monument, and to the east another such Upper Greensand bench projects northward from the foot of St. Martins Down, ending in a wooded scarp at Cook's Castle.

To the right, Worsley Trail descends along the edge of a field that, when ploughed, shows cloddy Gault clay. Gat Cliff (534805) is a steep scrubby slope (Fig. 84) with some layered outcrops of cherty beds near the top, and many small terracettes (page 59) on a steep grassy slope (Fig. 17), fronted by hummocky landslides, which are crossed by the sandy footpath. Worsley Trail runs beyond Gat Cliff, down to gates into Appuldurcombe Park, where below the Gault there are benches on the Carstone and the Sandrock. A footpath leads down into the Eastern Yar valley at Wroxall.

The lane beside Wroxall church climbs over the old railway bridge to a footpath over a stile. This edges along the rising Upper Greensand scarp, scrubby and wooded, to Cook's Castle (558805), on the well-defined structural bench below the rising Chalk escarpment of St. Martins Down. There is a view back to the equivalent feature at Gat Cliff on the Upper Greensand bench above Appuldurcombe, backed by the Chalk scarp rising to the radio mast on Appuldurcombe Down.

It is possible at this point to take the southward track, up St. Martin's Down, and follow the Lower Chalk ridge to Luccombe Down, round to St. Boniface Down, and complete a circuit by descending into Ventnor.

Alternatively, Worsley Trail continues along the top of the Upper Greensand breakaway, which has segments of cherty sandstone cliff and crag on the wooded slope at Cliff Copse (570804). The escarpment of the Lower Chalk then recedes behind a broad, deep valley, headed by Greatwood Copse. The Upper Greensand bench curves round into this valley, and on the slopes to the east are hummocky landslides on the Gault, continuing above Knock Cliff on the Luccombe spur.

Worsley Trail descends a spur across rumpled Gault. There are views across Shanklin, with ridges on the Sandrock Beds at Sibden Hill and to the west, over the lowlands in the axis of the Sandown Anticline to the south-facing Greensand and Chalk escarpments rising to Brading Hill. Beyond Sandown Pier is the white chalk of Culver Cliff, with the Anvil standing out as a bench at the eastern end. The footpath goes down to a stile, and through St. Blasius churchyard to Church Road, which runs on down across the Sandrock Beds to the Old Village by Shanklin Chine.

Excursion 9

A Walk above St. Lawrence

From St. Lawrence (533764) a track runs up to cross Seven Sisters Road to a steep zig-zag path that leads on up through woodland to a cliff cut in the cherty sandstones of the Upper Greensand (Fig. 86). At the top is a good viewpoint (532765). There is open grassland, with higher brows of Lower Chalk, furrowed by small coombes that converge northward into the Eastern Yar valley running down through Whitwell. To the west is the undulating crest of the breakaway, which continues past the radio masts to the Niton Gap. Southward the view is down into the Undercliff, with the tilted Upper Greensand bank at Woody Point in the foreground, and the subsided terraces of Ventnor to the east. From the radio masts there is a view down across the slumping slopes to Binnel Bay, with hummocky topography extending to the lighthouse on St. Catherine's Point. The topography is shown in the cross-section in Fig. 19.

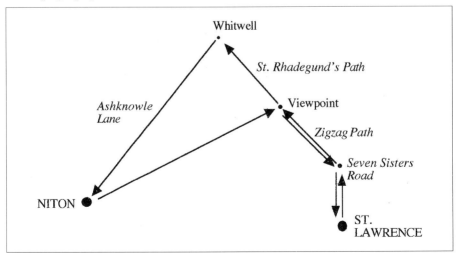

Fig. 86: Excursion 9.

St. Rhadegund's Path runs north-west, down a valley cut through the Chalk and Upper Greensand to the Gault. Springs mark the rise of a headstream of the Eastern Yar. Just before Whitwell church, Ashknowle Lane (523776) branches to the left along a steep slope below the Chert Beds of the Upper Greensand, and up on the eastern side of the col at Niton. It joins the Coastal Footpath (506762), which can be followed eastward along the southern edge of the plateau, climbing on to the Lower Chalk at the crest of the cliff, which faces southward and overlooks the hummocky terrain of St. Catherine's Point. The circuit is completed at the viewpoint (532765), before descending to St Lawrence.

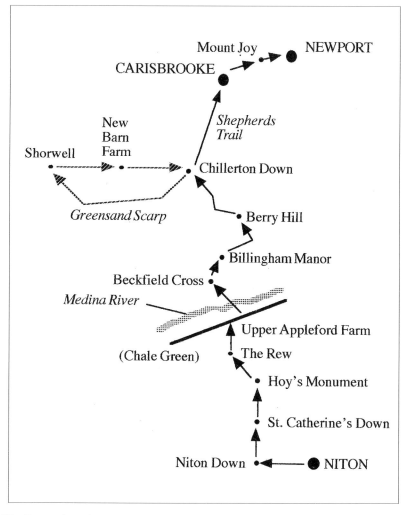

Fig. 87: Excursion 10

Excursion 10

A Walk from Niton to Newport

The varied structure and scenery of the southern part of the Isle of Wight is well illustrated along a walk from Niton up and along St. Catherine's Hill, across to Kingston, north to Chillerton Down, and on down Shepherds Trail to Carisbrooke and Newport (Fig. 87).

South of Niton the Coastal Footpath can be found at Boxers Lane (506763) and followed along the top of West Cliff, past the radio station to the top of Gore Cliff. Here the layered chert beds of the Upper Greensand are exposed in a vertical cliff overlooking the landslides that descend to St. Catherine's Point and Rocken End. Masses of Lower Chalk and Upper Greensand have subsided over the Gault, the Lower Greensand emerging to form cliffs to the west of Rocken End.

To the north is the Lower Chalk escarpment rising to Niton Down. The Coastal Footpath curves inland above Blackgang, where the chert beds cliff fades into a steep Upper Greensand scarp that runs inland and northward. From the upper car park there is a fine view across Chale to the lowlands on Lower Greensand and the Wealden Beds behind Brighstone Bay, backed by the Upper Greensand and Chalk escarpments that run westward past Shorwell, Brighstone and Mottistone to the cliffs of Compton Bay. Beside the car park is a section showing the junction between the Upper Greensand and the base of the Lower Chalk.

Across the A3055 a footpath climbs across the Upper Greensand bench on Gore Down and up the Chalk escarpment to the octagonal greenstone tower of St. Catherine's Oratory. The summit of St. Catherine's Hill is 236 metres above sea level, and has a small capping of angular flint gravel, a remnant of the extensive superficial deposits that formerly mantled an upland plain, 230-240 metres above present sea level (page 51), which has been deeply dissected by river valleys. There is a view to the east across the Whitwell valley, cut by a headstream of the Eastern Yar, to the long Chalk ridge that ascends from Week Down to Appuldurcombe Down, where the Chalk escarpment descends to the Upper Greensand bench that terminates in steep Gat Cliff. To the west the Chalk escarpment descends, past a large excavated hollow, to the Upper Greensand bench, below which is a steep grassy slope broken by occasional cliffy outcrops in the chert beds (Fig. 86), including Tolt Rocks (491773), which have been modified by quarrying. The slopes descend to gentler, hummocky landslide topography which developed under periglacial conditions in Late Pleistocene and early Holocene times when recurrent freezing and thawing, together with the effects of melting snow, made these slopes unstable, the Upper Greensand disintegrating into large masses that slid down over the lubricated Gault clay. This zone of former landslides, now generally stable, extends round under the Lower Greensand bench to the north, and is seen also beneath Gat Cliff and St. Martin's Down on the northern fringes of the Southern Plateau.

North from St. Catherine's Hill a trackway descends the Chalk escarpment to a long spur of Upper Greensand, a steep-sided, narrow embankment that ends in a sudden drop below Hoy's Monument, with a curved hollow where the land has subsided. This Upper Greensand scarp is much like Gat Cliff and Cook's Castle to the east, and below it is hummocky landslide topography of broken greensand over the largely concealed Gault. Three outlying knolls around Upper Dolcoppice (503794) are capped by Carstone. A footpath to the left goes down to the little valley of The Rew (493794), incised into a sloping bench on the Sandrock Beds. This has been dissected into spurs which have cappings of angular flint and chert gravel about 95 metres above sea level, probably remnants of an early valley floor of the upper Medina River, which rises near Chale Green.

Fig. 88: The Upper Greensand escarpment north of Tolt Rocks on the western side of St. Catherine's Hill, with some outcrops of the Chert Beds.

A footpath to the north descends from the Sandrock Beds bench past Upper Appleford Farm, on to the Ferruginous Sands, which here occupy the broad lowland on either side of the incised Medina valley. The footpath reaches a lane (495803), and if this is followed to the right for about 400 yards another footpath (498804), to the left, runs across to the Medina River below the Sewage Works (491806). The landscape is dominated by a terrace about 70 metres above sea level, into which the Medina valley and its tributaries are incised. Below the Sewage Works the present valley floor of the Medina is 50 metres above sea level, descending north-eastward through the swampy sector known as The Wilderness.

Across the Medina valley the footpath climbs on to the river terrace, and then ascends a gentle slope to Beckfield Cross (482810), near Kingston. A small but well-defined west-facing escarpment can be traced southward from here to South Down (476786), west of Chale, where it ends abruptly. As previously noted (page 59), this escarpment corresponds with a sandstone within the area mapped as Ferruginous Sands, and is probably developed on the permeable Sands of Walpen Undercliff over the impermeable Foliated Clay and Sand as the result of undercutting by groundwater seepage.

North from Beckfield Cross a lane leads across a slight valley in the upper Ferruginous Sands up to Billingham Manor, which is overlooked by the south-facing escarpment of the Sandrock Beds, capped by Carstone. Just north of the Manor (485821)a footpath, Shepherd's Trail, runs off to the right beneath, and then up, the escarpment, and over to the gentle dip-slope, along the edge of a wood to a lane that runs beneath the cherty Upper Greensand escarpment at Berry Hill and Rams Down (491833).

This south-facing Upper Greensand chert escarpment, backed by a dip-slope that descends to the base of the Chalk escarpment, extends east and west from Berry Hill. To the left, the lane runs north-west to join a road that runs through a gap in the Upper Greensand chert escarpment (483828), and a track to the left (482829) crosses to the old quarries in Lower and Middle Chalk on the escarpment at Chillerton Down (Fig. 89).

It is possible here to make a westward detour by taking a footpath to the left, diagonally up the Upper Greensand dip slope and follow the crest of the Upper Greensand Chert Beds escarpment westward to Shorwell (Fig. 90). The view southward is across the Gault valley to a dissected bench on the Carstone and Sandrock Beds between Billingham Manor and Heath Hill, south-east of Shorwell. Beyond this the land declines to a broad lowland on Ferruginous Sands, within which are smaller scarps on resistant sandstone components at Gun Hill (470813), Dungewood (465808) and Warren Hill (466805), seen on the walk described with Excursion 2.

Resuming in the valley south of Chillerton Down, a track continues past a gate and up the Chalk escarpment through grassy quarries where terracettes

Above, Fig. 89: View northward down the dip slope of the Upper Greensand to the Chalk escarpment on Chillerton Down.

Below, Fig. 90: View eastward along the Upper Greensand escarpment east of Shorwell towards Berry Hill, with the Chalk escarpment of Chillerton Down on the left.

have already formed on the abandoned quarry slopes. On the summit of Chillerton Down, 167 metres above sea level, stands the tall television mast. Exposures at the top of the old quarries show shattered Middle Chalk with a thin dark rendzina soil, but the plateau running north has a capping of angular flint gravel. This plateau may be a remnant of a land surface originally cut at this level by a Pliocene sea (page 51). The footpath descends gradually northward to a slight col above the pines of Dukem Copse, and from here (475849) a track runs down the side of a deep dry valley incised into the Chalk escarpment to Newbarn Farm. The Upper Greensand bench is prominent to the east of the farm, incised by the valley that curves eastward, descending to the Gault at Gatcombe. The Upper Greensand chert escarpment is steep, and from its base issue springs that feed a small stream flowing down to join the Medina River.

A footpath (Shepherd's Trail) from Newbarn Farm runs northward, up the steep slope of the Chert Beds, and then diagonally across the Upper Greensand dip-slope bordering the valley of Lukely Brook to Whitcombe Cross (487874). The steepening northward dip rapidly narrows the outcrops of the geological formations from west to east. To the north, across a dry valley in the Lower and Middle Chalk, is Carisbrooke Castle on a knoll of Upper Chalk, the escarpment of which rises to Bowcombe Down, beyond the valley of Lukely Brook. This brook has cut a gap through the Upper Chalk ridge at Carisbrooke, and from Whitcombe Cross a road runs through a second dry valley east of Carisbrooke Castle hill, a footpath (489877) to the right climbing over Mount Joy, another segment of Chalk to the east, with views across the Medina River gap at Shide before descending into Newport.

Excursion 11

A Walk from Mottistone Down to Brighstone Bay

The series of geological formations that outcrop south of the western part of the Central Downs can be examined in a walk from Mottistone Down (Fig. 91). This is readily accessible from the car park (420846) above Brighstone, whence Tennyson Trail runs west to the summit of Mottistone Down (203 metres) on northward-dipping Upper Chalk capped by angular flint gravel. A footpath (407847) descends the escarpment of Middle and Lower Chalk southward, to run along the edge of a woodland across the head of a valley cut out along the narrow Upper Greensand and Gault outcrops. The track then climbs on to the ridge of heathy Mottistone Common (where the pinewoods have been largely cleared), capped by the Carstone and Sandrock Beds, to the Long Stone (407843), a Neolithic monument of ferruginous sandstone. To the east embankments enclose a square Iron Age fort on Castle Hill (140 metres).

The footpath then descends a wooded valley on the south-facing escarpment of the Ferruginous Sands (Fig. 92) to Mottistone Manor, built mainly of stone from the Greensands, including Carstone. Across the B3399 is the church of Sts. Peter and Paul (406837), built of similar material, and standing on a narrow outcrop of Atherfield Clay as the slope diminishes below the Ferruginous Sands escarpment. South of the church, Ridget Lane runs southward down a gentle slope on Vectis Shales (upper part of Wealden Beds) to the Military Road, A3055, in the broad shallow gravel-floored Sudmoor valley that declines gradually westward to Brook.

Across this road the footpath continues for a short distance on slightly rising ground to the crest of the cliff cut in Wessex Marls (lower part of Wealden Beds), overlooking Brighstone Bay (401825). Below is a sandy beach, and at low tide a shore platform of red sandstone, carpeted with seaweed, is exposed.

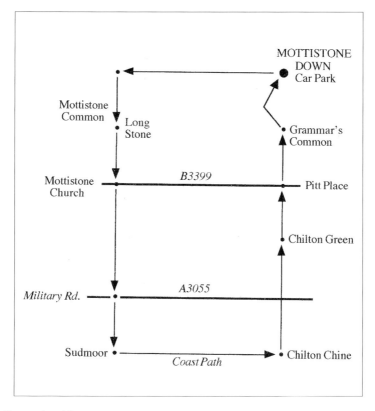

Fig. 91: Excursion 11.

The Coastal Footpath is then followed eastward to Chilton Chine, a valley incised into the Wessex Marls, dipping gently east-north-eastward (page 118). The gravel deposits of the Sudmoor valley are seen in the crest of the cliff. A footpath runs inland, through the car park and across the Military Road, following the incised valley up to Chilton Green. From here Hoxall Lane runs northward, and Pitt Place Lane (414826) diverges from it, climbing the slope to the B3399. Gravels mantle the Wealden Beds on the rising slope, and the gradient steepens across the Atherfield Clay at Pitt Place.

A little to the east along the B3399 a footpath (416834) leads northward up the escarpment of the Ferruginous Sands to Grammar's Common (137 metres), curving through woodland and over to Strawberry Lane. Here it descends a slope in Sandrock Beds and Carstone into a wide valley cut down to the Gault, before climbing diagonally across the Upper Greensand and Chalk escarpment, back to the car park.

Fig. 92: The escarpment of the Ferruginous Sands (Lower Greensand) north of Mottistone.

Excursion 12

The Country around Newbridge

Features in the western part of the northern lowlands can be seen on a drive from Newbridge (412876), on the B3401 south of Yarmouth (Fig. 93). Newbridge stands on the northern edge of the Bembridge Limestone outcrop, in a landscape that is gently undulating, dissected by the valleys of streams that flow northward into Newtown Harbour. A short way to the east Quarry Lane (418876) diverges from the B3401 to follow a small north-facing scarp of this limestone on the ridge running eastward along Quarry Lane to Five Houses. Bembridge Limestone outcrops in an old quarry at 422877, and is also seen below the hedge bordering Elm Lane as it descends the scarp southward to Langbridge Farm. East of Five Houses the Bembridge Limestone fades out, and the junction between the soft Headon Beds and the similar Bembridge Marls has no topographic expression.

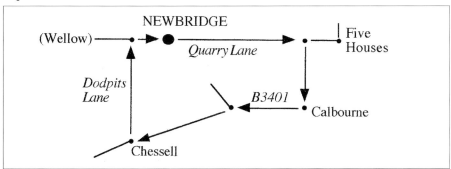

Fig 93: Excursion 12.

From the cross-roads (426877) a lane runs southward across the Eocene formations until the Upper Chalk emerges from the edge of the Reading Beds at Calbourne. The dip is gentle, and near the edge of the Reading Beds are some small depressions formed by solution of the Upper Chalk surface, and partly filled with soil. Chalk country rises to the south, but B3401 runs west to a fork (420869), where a left turning crosses a wide shallow valley on the Bagshot Beds to Chessell (397858). From here Dodgpits Lane turns northward down the western side of the Caul Bourne valley, beside a broad and gentle dip-slope on the Bembridge Limestone south of Wellow (387882). This has been exposed by the removal of formerly overlying Bembridge Marls, and is a good example of a structurally-guided landform. The lane descends to the edge of the Bembridge Marls at its junction with the B3401, which runs eastward back into Newbridge.

Notes

1. H.J. Osborne White (1921) *A short account of the geology of the Isle of Wight*. British Geological Survey. Reprinted 1994. See also C.P. Chatwin (1960) *The Hampshire Basin and adjoining areas*. British Regional Geology.

2. B. Daley and A. Insole (1984) *The Isle of Wight*. Geologists' Association Guide No. 25.

3. Surface heights and contours on the Ordnance Survey Isle of Wight map are to the nearest metre above mean sea level.

4. A dip-slope is one which corresponds precisely with the angle of the dipping strata. The term back-slope is used for a slope that declines in the same direction as the strata, but actually truncates them at a low angle.

5. R. Fortey (1993) *The Hidden Landscape*. Pimlico, London.

6. Weathering is the physical disintegration, chemical decomposition and biological modification of rock formations when they are exposed to the atmosphere.

7. N. Pevsner and D. Lloyd (1967) *Hampshire and the Isle of Wight*. The Buildings of England. Penguin, Harmondsworth.

8. The Isle of Wight has long been a centre for Geological Excursions, some of which have been reported in the *Proceedings of the Geologists' Association*. See for example F.C. Stinton (1971) Excursion to the Isle of Wight, vol. 82: 403-410, and B. Daley and D.J. Stewart (1979) Week-end field meeting, the Wealden Group in the Isle of Wight, vol. 90: 51-54.

9. E.C.F. Bird (1995) *Geology and Scenery of Dorset*. Ex Libris Press, Bradford on Avon.

10. D. Stewart (1981) A meander-belt sandstone of the Lower Cretaceous of Southern England, *Sedimentology*, 28: 1-20.

11. Details of the Pine Raft are given in the *Geological Memoir* (Note 1): 8.

12. Now *Mulletia mulletti*.

13. Ferruginous means rich in iron compounds. See Note 22.

14. W.H. Fitton (1847) A stratigraphical account of the section from Atherfield to Rocken End on the south-west coast of the Isle of Wight, *Quarterly Journal of the Geological Society*, 3: 289-327.

15. The Gault and Upper Greensand together constitute the Selbornian, named by A.J. Jukes-Brown in 1900 from their occurrence at Selborne in Hampshire. The proportion of the two formations varies, the Gault clay becoming thinner and sandier from east to west through Southern England.

16. The Chalk Rock was originally described from the Middle Chalk of Berkshire and Wiltshire, where it is found at lower horizon than in the Isle of Wight. The Melbourn Rock originally described in Cambridgeshire, and prominent in the Chiltern Hills, is more massive than that seen at the base of the Middle Chalk of the Isle of Wight. See *Geological Memoir* (Note 1): 61, 63.

17. Details of the palaeontological zones of the chalk are given in the *Geological Memoir* (Note 1): 55.

18. R.L. Sherlock (1960) *London and the Thames valley*. British Regional Geology: 26-36.

19. C. King (1981) *The stratigraphy of the London Clay and associated deposits, Tertiary Research*, Special Paper No. 6.

20. F. Buurman (1980) Palaeosols in the Reading Beds (Palaeocene) of Alum Bay, Isle of Wight, *Sedimentology, 27*: 593-606.

21. The Oldhaven Beds were named from Oldhaven Gap (now known as Bishopstone Haven) east of Herne Bay on the North Kent coast, where they are a sandy equivalent of the Blackheath Pebble Beds, immediately below the London Clay. W. Whitaker (1866) On the Lower London Tertiaries of Kent, *Quarterly Journal of the Geological Society*, 22: 413-429.

22. Haematite is an iron sesquioxide (Fe_2O_3) and limonite a hydrated iron sesquioxide ($Fe_2O_3. 2H_2O$).

23. See *Geological Memoir* (Note 1): 114.

24. B. Daley (1973) The palaeoenvironment of the Bembridge Marls, (Oligocene) of the Isle of Wight, *Proceedings of the Geologists' Association*, 84: 83-93.

25. Sub-surface contours are shown the Hydrogeological map of Hampshire and the Isle of Wight published by the Institute of Geological

Sciences & Southern Water Authority (1979).

26. Little is known of the distribution of these post-Oligocene sediments on the floor of the English Channel, which maps of submarine geology show to be dominated by early Tertiary, Cretaceous and Jurassic outcrops.

27. There are no reliable long-term tide gauge records in the Isle of Wight, but measurements at Newlyn in Cornwall have shown a rise of mean sea level averaging 2.4 millimetres per year since 1916-21, and if this is typical of the south coast of England it may indicate that subsidence is in progress.

28. Estimates by A.J. Jukes-Brown (1906) The Clay with Flints: its origin and distribution, *Quarterly Journal of the Geological Society*, 62: 132-164.

29. Reference is made to Palaeolithic implements in the Plateau Gravel in the *Geological Memoir* (Note 1): 151-161.

30. J. Prestwich (1892) The raised beaches and 'Head' or rubble-drift of the south of England, Quarterly Journal of the Geological Society, 48: 263-343. See also H.G. Dines (1940) The mapping of Head deposits, *Geological Magazine, 77*: 198-226.

31. An example of gravel spread by solifluction in Dorset was given by E.C.F Bird (1973) The periglacial legacy in the Weymouth lowland, *Biuletyn Peryglacjalny*, 22: 315-321.

32. G. Colenutt (1929) The cliff-founder and landslide at Gore Cliff, Isle of Wight. *Proceedings of the Isle of Wight Natural History and Archaeological Society, 1*: 561-570. For a recent account see E.N. Brodhead et al. (1991) in R.J. Chandler (ed.) *Slope Stability Engineering*, Telford, London: 189-196.

33. R.C. Preece (1980) The biostratigraphy and dating of a slope deposit on Gore Cliff near Blackgang, Isle of Wight, *Journal of Archaeological Science, 7*: 255-265.

34. W. Fox (1862) When and how was the Isle of Wight separated from the mainland? *The Geologist, 5*: 452-454.

35. C. Reid (1902) Geology of the country around Ringwood, *Memoirs of the Geological Survey*: 31-32.

36. C. Lyell (1830) *Principles of Geology. vol. 1*, p. 279.

37. A distinction should be made between the age of outcropping geological formations and the age of the land surface cut across them. Thus in the Isle of Wight the outcrops range in age from Lower Cretaceous to Lower Tertiary, but the present landscape is largely of Quaternary age, with a few features possibly inherited from the Upper Tertiary.

38. S.W. Wooldridge and D.L. Linton (1955) Structure, Surface and Drainage in South-east England. *Institute of British Geographers: 43.*

39. A marine origin for the upland plain in Dorset was proposed by A.J. Jukes-Brown (1895) The origin of valleys of the Chalk Downs of North Dorset, *Proceedings of the Dorset Natural History and Archaeological Society, 16*: 5-13.

40. C.P. Green (1974) The summit surface of the Wessex Chalk, in E.H. Brown and R.S. Waters (eds.) *The Shaping of Southern England. Academic Press*, London: 172-202.

41. S.W. Wooldridge and D.L. Linton (1955) Structure, Surface and Drainage in South-east England. *Institute of British Geographers: 73.*

42. The Lenham Beds have since been dated Lower Pleistocene, which implies that the marine planation may be of Pleistocene rather than Pliocene age. See D.K.C. Jones (1981) *Southeast and Southern England*. Methuen.

43. C.E. Everard (1954) The Solent River: a geomorphological study. *Transactions of the Institute of British Geographers, 20*: 41-54.

44. Details of the Bembridge Raised Beach are given in the *Geological Memoir* (Note 1): 160-161. See also K.H. Davies and D.H. Keen (1985) The age of Pleistocene marine deposits at Portland, Dorset, *Proceedings of the Geologists' Association, 96*: 217-225.

45. It would be interesting to know when and why these embankments were constructed.

46. The Holocene has also been called the Postglacial, which is appropriate in formerly glaciated areas such as northern Britain. In the Isle of Wight it is strictly the Post-periglacial. However, as ice persists in polar and mountain regions, the Earth is really still in a Glacial phase.

47. C.E. Everard (1956) Erosion platforms on the borders of the Hampshire Basin. *Transactions of the Institute of British Geographers, 22*: 33-46.

48. The Late Quaternary marine transgression is known in Europe as the Flandrian transgression because it was first documented in Flanders.

49. H. Valentin (1953) Present vertical movements of the British Isles, *Geographical Journal, 119*: 299-305.

50. W.H. Ward (1962) Coastal cliffs - report of a Symposium, *Geographical Journal, 128*: 311-312.

51. Instability in the St. Lawrence area was noted by R.G. McInnes (1994) A Management Strategy for the Coastal Zone. South Wight Borough Council, Isle of Wight. See also papers by E.M. Lee et al. in R.J. Chandler (ed.) *Slope Stability Engineering*, Telford, London: 207-212 and 218-225. References to other recent papers on landslides between Luccombe and Blackgang are given in the Department of the Environment book *Landsliding in Great Britain* (H.M.S.O. 1994).

52. J.N. Hutchinson, M.P. Chandler and E.N. Bromhead (1981) Cliff recession on the Isle of Wight south-west coast, *Proceedings of the 10th International Conference on Soil Mechanics and Foundation Engineering*: 429-434.

53. R.F. Moorman (1939) Notes on the principal 'mud glacier' at Hamstead, *Proceedings of the Isle of Wight Natural History Society, 3*: 148-150.

54. R.J. Allison (1992) Landslide types and processes, in R.J. Allison (ed.) *The Coastal Landforms of West Dorset*: 35-49.

55. Beach sources in the Isle of Wight are similar to those on the Dorset coast. See E.C.F. Bird (1989) The beaches of Lyme Bay *Proceedings of the Dorset Natural History and Archaeological Society, 111*: 91-97.

56. Evidence of coastline changes can also be obtained from early photographs and paintings. See R. McInnes (1990) *The Garden Isle*. McInnes and Cross, Isle of Wight.

57. V. May and C. Heeps (1985) The nature and rates of change on chalk coastlines, *Zeitschrift für Geomorphologie, Supplement band 57*: 81-94.

58. R.G. McInnes (1994) *A Management Strategy for the Coastal Zone*. South Wight Borough Council, Isle of Wight.

59. Sir John Oglander described Barnsley Harbour in 1623, as quoted in Eric Bird and Lilian James (1992) *Writers on the Coast*. Windrush, Gloucestershire: 147.

60. The features of Brading Harbour in the 19th century are shown in paintings by Clarkson Stanfield in the 1830s (*The Garden Isle*, Plate 20, p. 49) and Alfred Vickers around 1850 (*The Garden Isle*, Plate 22, p. 53).

61. The Bembridge Raised Beach is described in the *Geological Memoir* (Note 1): 161.

62. G.W. Colenutt (1939) *Proceedings of the Isle of Wight Natural History Society*, 3: 50, quoted by J.A. Steers (1964) *The Coastline of England and Wales*. 2nd edition. Cambridge: 638.

63. S.W. Wooldridge and F. Goldring (1953) *The Weald*. Collins New Naturalist, London.

64. The Lower Chalk here consists of about 54 metres of stratified Grey Chalk (grey and white limestone with thin grey marls) over 20 metres of less stratified Chalk Marl (blue-grey mottled marls and thin grey limestones), with about 2.5 metres of glauconitic marl at the base.

65. This yellow sandstone has been correlated with the Barnes High Sandstone seen in the cliffs of Brighstone Bay (p. 27).

66. The Exogyra Sandstone is named after its dominant fossil, *Exogyra sinuata*.

67. A tombolo is a spit that attaches an island (in this case an artificial nearshore rock wall) to the mainland.

68. The Gore Cliff sketch is reproduced as Fig. 13 in the *Geological Memoir* (Note 1): 51.

69. A hanging valley is one that has been truncated so that it ends in a notch in the cliff, sometimes with a stream descending as a waterfall. See Fig. 56.

70. The Pine Raft is a Cretaceous formation, not a 'submerged forest' in the sense that the term has been widely used in Southern England for intertidal and sea floor relics of much younger (Pleistocene to early Holocene) woodlands submerged during the Late Quaternary marine transgression.

71. Lulworth Cove and Arish Mell Gap are illustrated in E.C.F. Bird (1995) *Geology and Scenery of Dorset*: 178-179 and 181.

72. The grass is mainly *Spartina anglica*, a hybrid between a native species, *Spartina maritima* and *Spartina alterniflora*, an American species (presumably brought in on a ship's hull) which appeared on Hythe marsh, Southampton Water, in about 1870. It has since spread, or been introduced, to the Isle of Wight estuaries and other estuaries in Southern England and elsewhere.

73. Isle of Wight County Council (1952), quoted by J.A. Steers (1964) *The Coastline of England and Wales*. 2nd edition. Cambridge: 638.

74. Spring sapping is erosion by the washing-out of sediment along a seepage zone.

INDEX

Also by Eric Bird and uniform with THE SHAPING OF THE ISLE OF WIGHT:

GEOLOGY AND SCENERY OF DORSET

This book aims to introduce the reader to the geological basis of the varied scenery of Dorset, a county composed of a succession of sedimentary rocks – some hard, some soft and often folded and faulted. It is this diversity which largely determines the County's ever-changing landscape – its hills, vales, moors, rivers and its remarkable coastal scenery.

Dorset's fossil heritage is well known to many, though fewer are familiar with the connection between the county's scenery and its underlying rocks. Dorset contains many textbook examples of geological structures and landscape forms; its long coastline and innumerable quarries provide ample opportunity to inspect the naked rock. It is no idle boast that Dorset is known as the cradle of English geology.

Eric Bird's book is a comprehensive introduction to the geology of Dorset. He begins with some basic definitions, guides us through the last 250 million years of rock strata as found locally, explains the more recent evolution of the landscape and finally offers a dozen excursions which may be completed by car and/or on foot. These form the basis of a thorough survey of the entire spectrum of the county's geology and landscape.

The Geology and Scenery of Dorset provides an informative and practical companion to discovering and understanding the intimate relationship between landscape and geology.

31 Maps, diagrams and cross-sections; 58 Photographs; Notes, References and Index; 207 pages; Price £8.95

Also by Eric Bird, with Lilian Modlock:

WRITERS ON THE SOUTH-WEST COAST
A Literary Journey from Dorset via Land's End to the Bristol Channel

The south-west peninsula includes England's most beautiful coastline: wild craggy headlands, wind-swept sand-dunes and magnificent drowned valleys all contribute to a richly varied seascape and habitat. Reaching westward towards the Atlantic Ocean, it is not surprising that the life of this part of the country has traditionally been bound up with the sea. Fishing, shipbuilding, privateering, overseas trade and emigration have all flourished.

The region's combination of natural beauty and human history has acted as an inspiration to writers for many years. Famous names are legion: Daniel Defoe, Wilkie Collins, Thomas Hardy, the Powys brothers, John Betjeman, Daphne Du Maurier and John Fowles are some of the more well known whose work features in this book. Yet the compilers of this anthology have not been content merely to include the more obvious candidates. They have searched out a host of literary gems from a wide range of authors.

To read this book is indeed to embark upon a literary journey around the entire south-west coast, including an excursion to the Isles of Scilly. Certain places and voices will be familiar, others not so. The sum of the parts adds up to a most satisfying whole, so that *Writers on the South West Coast*, under the well-informed direction of the joint compilers, provides an ideal companion both to the armchair traveller and to the literary pilgrim in the field. Lilian Modlock's many illustrations, drawn specially for this volume, add to the delights of the journey.

285 pages; Illustrated throughout; Price £8.95

In addition, Ex Libris Press publishes around 50 titles dealing with the south west of England, the Channel Islands and country life, including the WEST COUNTRY LANDSCAPES series. Please ask for our free illustrated catalogue.

EX LIBRIS PRESS books are available through local bookshops or may be obtained direct from the publisher, post-free, on receipt of net price, at

1 The Shambles, Bradford on Avon, Wiltshire, BA15 lJS

Tel/Fax 01225 863595